Claire Hutchinson

D1454451

ESSENTIALS
OCR GCSE
Physics B

Contents

Contents

Fundamental Scientific Processes

Scientists carry out **experiments** and collect **evidence** in order to explain how and why things happen. Scientific knowledge and understanding can lead to the **development of new technologies** which have a huge impact on **society** and the **environment**.

Scientific evidence is often based on data that has been collected through **observations** and **measurements**. To allow scientists to reach conclusions, evidence must be **repeatable**, **reproducible** and **valid**.

Models

Models are used to explain scientific ideas and the universe around us. Models can be used to describe:

- a complex idea like how heat moves through a metal
- a system like the Earth's structure.

Models make a system or idea easier to understand by only including the most important parts. They can be used to explain real world observations or to make predictions. But, because models don't contain all the variables, they do sometimes make incorrect predictions.

Models and scientific ideas may change as new observations are made and new data are collected. Data and observations may be collected from a series of experiments. For example, the accepted model of the structure of the atom has been modified as new evidence has been collected from many experiments.

Hypotheses

Scientific explanations are called hypotheses. Hypotheses are used to explain observations. A hypothesis can be tested by planning experiments and collecting data and evidence. For example, if you pull a metal wire you may observe that it stretches. This can be explained by the scientific idea that the atoms in the metal are in layers and can slide over each other. A hypothesis can be modified as new data is collected, and may even be disproved.

Data

Data can be displayed in **tables**, **pie charts** or **line graphs**. In your exam you may be asked to:

- choose the most appropriate method for displaying data
- identify trends
- use the data mathematically, including using statistical methods, calculating the **mean** and calculating gradients of graphs.

Pie Chart

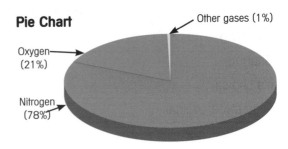

Other gases (1%)
Oxygen (21%)
Nitrogen (78%)

Line Graph

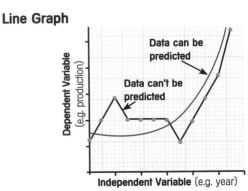

Data can be predicted
Data can't be predicted
Dependent Variable (e.g. production)
Independent Variable (e.g. year)

Table

Pressure (Atmospheres)	Yield (%) Temperature (°C)			
	250	350	450	550
200	73	50	28	13
400	77	65	45	26

Model • Variable • Data • Hypothesis

Data (Cont.)

Sometimes the same data can lead to different conclusions. For example, data shows that the world's average temperatures have been rising significantly over the last 200 years. Some scientists think this is due to increased combustion of fossil fuels, whilst other scientists think it's a natural change seen before in Earth's history.

Scientific and Technological Development

Every scientific or technological development could have effects that we do not know about. This can give rise to **issues**. An issue is an important question that is in dispute and needs to be settled. Issues could be:

- **Social** – they impact on the human population of a community, city, country, or the world.
- **Environmental** – they impact on the planet, its natural ecosystems and resources.
- **Economic** – money and related factors like employment and the distribution of resources.
- **Cultural** – what is morally right and wrong; a value judgement must be made.

Peer review is a process of self-regulation involving experts in a particular field who **critically examine** the work undertaken. Peer review methods are designed to maintain standards and provide **credibility** for the work that has been carried out. The methods used vary depending on the type of work and also on the overall purpose behind the review process.

Evaluating Information

Conclusions can then be made based on the scientific evidence that has been collected and should try to explain the results and observations.

Evaluations look at the whole investigation. It is important to be able to evaluate information relating to social-scientific issues. When evaluating information:

- make a list of **pluses** (pros)
- make a list of **minuses** (cons)
- consider how each point might **impact on society**.

You also need to consider whether the source of information is reliable and credible and consider opinions, bias and weight of evidence.

Opinions are personal viewpoints. Opinions backed up by valid and reliable evidence carry far more weight than those based on non-scientific ideas. Opinions of experts can also carry more weight than opinions of non-experts. Information is **biased** if it favours one particular viewpoint without providing a balanced account. Biased information might include incomplete evidence or try to influence how you interpret the evidence.

P1 Heating Houses

Temperature

Temperature is a measure of how **hot** something is. The unit of measurement is degrees Celsius (°C). Temperature can be represented by a range of colours in a thermogram. Hottest areas appear white/yellow/red; coldest areas appear black/dark blue/purple.

Heat is a measurement of **energy** and is measured in joules (J).

> (HT) **Temperature** is a measurement of how hot something is using an arbitrary or **chosen scale**, usually degrees Celsius, Kelvin or sometimes degrees Fahrenheit (°F).
>
> The temperature of an object is a measurement of the average kinetic energy of the particles in that object.
>
> Heat is a measurement of energy on an **absolute scale**, always joules.

In this thermogram:
- the windows are where most heat energy is escaping – they show up as yellow
- the well-insulated loft is where the least heat energy is escaping – it shows up as purple.

Temperature Change

If there is a **difference** in temperature between an **object** and its **surroundings**, then **heat energy flows** from the hotter region to the cooler region.
- If an object's **temperature rises**, it is **taking in** heat energy. For example, if you take a can of cola out of the fridge it will soon warm up to room temperature, or **ambient temperature**, because the can takes in heat energy from the air in the room.
- If an object's **temperature falls**, it is **giving out** heat energy. For example, a hot cup of tea will cool down until it reaches room temperature. If you hold it in your hands you'll feel the heat energy flowing from the cup into your hands.

An object that has a very high temperature will cool down very quickly. As its temperature drops, it will cool down at a slower rate.

The rate of heating or cooling depends on the difference between the temperature of the object and the ambient temperature around it. The greater the difference, the greater the rate (and the steeper the curve on the graph).

Graph to show Temperature of a Cup of Tea

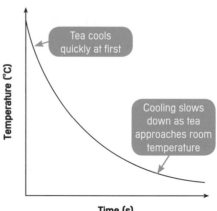

Tea cools quickly at first

Cooling slows down as tea approaches room temperature

Measuring Heat Energy

The amount of **energy** needed to raise the temperature of an object depends on:

- the **mass** of the object
- the **change** in temperature **required**
- the **material** it's made from.

The equipment shown alongside can be used to measure the amount of heat energy required to change the temperature of an aluminium block.

This 100W electric heater provides 100J of heat energy per second, i.e. 100J of heat energy passes into the aluminium every second.

Time how many seconds it takes for the temperature of the aluminium to rise by a certain amount, e.g. 10°C. You can then calculate the amount of energy used to bring about the change using this formula:

Total energy supplied	=	Energy supplied per second	×	Number of seconds

Example

It takes the heater 50 seconds to raise the temperature of the aluminium block by 10°C. Calculate the total energy supplied. Remember, the heater transfers 100J of heat energy per second.

$$\text{Total energy supplied} = \text{Energy supplied per second} \times \text{Number of seconds}$$
$$= 100\text{J/s} \times 50\text{s} = \textbf{5000J}$$

Thermometer — Power supply

Insulation — Electric heater — Aluminium block

The electric heater is known as the heat **source**.
The aluminium block is the heat **sink**.

Specific Heat Capacity

Each material has a value of how much energy it can hold. This is known as **specific heat capacity**.

Specific heat capacity is the energy needed to raise the temperature of 1kg of material by 1°C.

The following equation is used to find the amount of energy required to raise the temperature of an object by a certain amount.

Energy (J)	=	Mass (kg)	×	Specific heat capacity (J/kg°C)	×	Temperature change (°C)

(HT) You may be required to rearrange this equation to do a calculation.

Example

It takes 28 800J of heat energy to raise the temperature of a 4kg block of aluminium by 8°C. Calculate the specific heat capacity of aluminium.

$$\text{Specific heat capacity} = \frac{\text{Energy}}{\text{Mass} \times \text{Temperature change}}$$
$$= \frac{28\,800\text{J}}{4\text{kg} \times 8°\text{C}} = \textbf{900J/kg°C}$$

P1 Heating Houses

Melting and Boiling

Energy is needed to **melt** or **boil** substances. This is why the temperature of a material **doesn't change** when it's at the point of boiling, melting or freezing (i.e. **changing state**).

For example, the graph below shows how the temperature of a block of ice changes as it's heated up:

1. The temperature rises sharply to begin with.
2. Once it hits 0°C, it stops rising. This is because all the energy is being used to change the state of the ice from solid to liquid. The temperature stays at 0°C until **all** of the ice has melted.
3. The temperature rises until it reaches 100°C.
4. The temperature remains constant again, while the water changes state from liquid to gas (steam).

The temperature of water will never rise above 100°C, no matter how long it is heated for. But, the temperature of the gas (steam) produced from it can rise.

So, to interpret data that shows the heating or cooling of an object, look for places where the temperature stays the same.

HT During the melting and boiling of water, the energy supplied is used to **break intermolecular bonds** as the water molecules change state from solid to liquid, and from liquid to gas. This explains why the temperature of the material doesn't change.

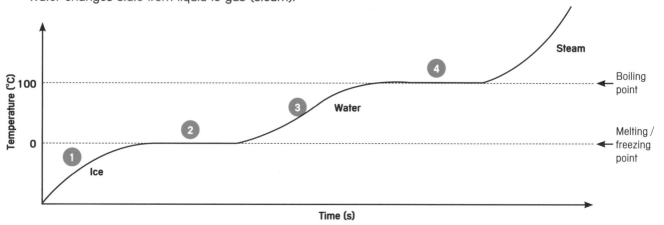

Specific Latent Heat

The amount of heat energy required to melt or boil 1kg of a material is called the **specific latent heat**.

It depends on:

- the **material**
- the **state** (solid, liquid or gas).

The energy required to boil or melt a certain mass of a material can be found using this equation:

> **Energy (J)** = **Mass (kg)** × **Specific latent heat (J/kg)**

Example

An ice sculpture with a mass of 10kg is left to melt on a hot day. The specific latent heat of ice is 330 000J/kg. Calculate the amount of energy required to melt the ice.

Energy = Mass × Specific latent heat
= 10kg × 330 000J/kg = **3 300 000J**

Quick Test

1. State the units of temperature and heat energy.
2. On a thermogram of two objects, one appears blue in colour and the other one is yellow. Which object is giving out the most heat energy?

Specific latent heat

Conductors and Insulators

Materials that allow energy to flow through them quickly are called **conductors**. Metals are good conductors.

Materials that allow energy to flow through them much more slowly are called **insulators**. Most non-metals, such as wood, plastic, glass and air are good insulators.

Curtains are good insulators because they **trap a layer of air** between them and the window, which helps reduce energy loss. Air is a good insulator because the particles are very far apart.

Saving Energy in the Home

Design features in the home help to **save energy** by reducing heat loss by **conduction**, **convection** and **radiation**. This table explains how.

Method of Insulation	Reduces:	How?
Fibreglass (or mineral wool) roof insulation	Conduction and convection	By trapping layers of air (a very good insulator) between the fibres.
Reflective foil on walls	Radiation	By reflecting heat energy back into the room.
Foam cavity wall insulation	Conduction and convection	By trapping air in the foam. (The air is an insulator and prevents conduction; being trapped stops it moving and so prevents convection.)
Double glazing	Conduction and convection	By trapping air between the panes of glass.
Draught excluders	Conduction and convection	By keeping as much warm air inside as possible.

Reducing Heat Loss in the Home

There are many different ways in which heat loss from a home can be **reduced**. Many insulation materials contain air, which is a very good insulator.

Method of Insulation	Cost	Annual Saving	Payback Time
Fibreglass roof insulation	£400	£80	5 years
Reflective foil on or in walls	£40	£10	4 years
Cavity wall insulation	£600	£30	20 years
Double glazing	£1800	£60	30 years
Draught excluders	£40	£20	2 years

An important consideration with each method is the **payback time**, i.e. how long it takes to pay for the insulation from the savings made.

$$\text{Payback time (in years)} = \frac{\text{Cost of installing insulation}}{\text{Annual saving}}$$

P1 Keeping Homes Warm

Cavity Wall Insulation

A **cavity wall** is made up of an inner and an outer wall separated by a cavity (space) filled with air. Trapped air is a good insulator, but in the cavity it is free to move.

The heat energy passes through the wall (from the radiator) by **conduction**. This heats the air in the cavity. The heat is then carried away from the wall by **convection**. Heat loss can be significantly reduced by filling the cavity with foam. The foam contains trapped air (a good insulator) so heat loss by conduction is reduced. The air is trapped in the foam, so heat loss by convection is reduced.

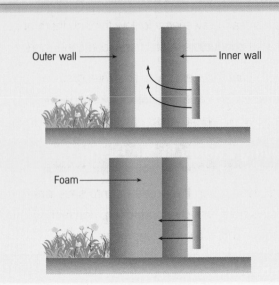

Energy Efficiency

Energy efficiency is a measure of how good an appliance is at **converting** input energy into **useful** output energy.

For example, the input energy for a television is electrical energy and the useful output energy is light and sound. But a television also produces heat energy, which is **wasted** energy, i.e. it isn't needed.

You can use this equation to calculate efficiency:

$$\text{Efficiency} = \frac{\text{Useful output energy (J)}}{\text{Total input energy (J)}} \times 100$$

Example
A 60 watt light bulb **uses** 60 joules of energy every second. Each second it **gives out** 6 joules of light energy. What is the efficiency of the light bulb?

$$\text{Efficiency} = \frac{\text{Useful output energy}}{\text{Total energy input}} \times 100$$

$$= \frac{6J}{60J} \times 100$$

$$= 0.1 \times 100 = \textbf{10\%}$$

This **Sankey diagram** shows the efficiency of a different light bulb.

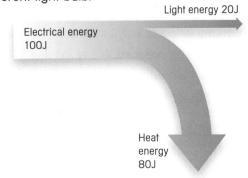

$$\text{Efficiency} = \frac{20J}{100J} \times 100 = 20\% \text{ efficient}$$

Transfer of Heat Energy

Air is a good **insulator**, because the particles are far apart. If air is trapped in a material, the material will be an insulator.

Heat energy doesn't stay in one place; it moves around. Hot air rises and is replaced by colder air. Heat energy can be transferred from one place to another by **conduction**, **convection** or **radiation**.

Transfer of Heat Energy (Cont.)

Here are some examples of how energy transfers are reduced in everyday situations:

- Kettles made of metal have shiny surfaces to reduce heat loss by radiation.

- Hot-water tanks are made of stainless steel and may also have a shiny outer layer to reduce heat loss by radiation. Hot-water tanks also usually have an insulating jacket to reduce heat loss by conduction and convection.

Conduction

Conduction is the transfer of heat energy **through a substance** from a hotter region to a cooler region without any movement of the substance itself.

(HT) As a substance, e.g. a metal poker, is heated, the kinetic energy of the particles increases. This kinetic energy is transferred between the particles and energy is transferred along the substance.

Metals have free electrons which can move through the material carrying energy. This makes metals very good conductors.

Transfer of Heat from Hotter to Cooler Region

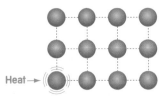

Quick Test

1. Which type of house insulation has the longest payback time?
2. Name the useful energies produced by a television.

Convection

Convection is the transfer of heat energy from hotter regions to cooler regions by the **movement of particles**.

(HT) As a liquid or gas gets hotter, its particles move faster, causing it to expand and become less dense. The particles in the hotter region will rise up and be replaced by particles from the colder, denser region.

Circulation of Air Caused by a Radiator

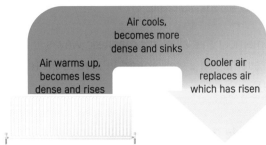

Air cools, becomes more dense and sinks

Air warms up, becomes less dense and rises

Cooler air replaces air which has risen

Radiation

Hot objects **emit** mainly **infra-red radiation**, an electromagnetic wave, which can pass through a vacuum, i.e. no medium is needed for its transfer. The amount of radiation given out or taken in by an object depends on its surface.

Dark matt surfaces emit more radiation than light shiny surfaces **at the same temperature**. Dark matt surfaces are better absorbers (poorer reflectors) of radiation than light shiny surfaces at the same temperature.

P1 A Spectrum of Waves

Light

Light is a **transverse wave**. A transverse wave has the following features:

- **Amplitude** – the maximum disturbance caused by the wave.
- **Wavelength** – the distance between corresponding points on two successive disturbances (e.g. from one crest to the next crest).
- **Frequency** – the number of waves produced (or that pass a particular point) in one second.

Crest, Amplitude, Wavelength, 0, 1 Time (s), Trough

Frequency = 4 waves per second

The Electromagnetic Spectrum

The **electromagnetic spectrum** is a continuous spectrum that extends beyond each end of the visible spectrum for light.

It includes **microwaves** and **infrared radiation**.

Radio waves
Microwaves
Infrared rays
Visible light
Ultraviolet rays
X-rays
Gamma rays

The Wave Equation

You can calculate the **speed** of a wave using this equation:

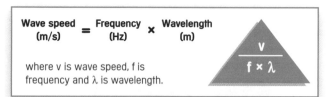

Wave speed (m/s) = **Frequency (Hz)** × **Wavelength (m)**

where v is wave speed, f is frequency and λ is wavelength.

$$\frac{v}{f \times \lambda}$$

But remember that all electromagnetic waves, including light, travel at the **same speed** in a **vacuum** (e.g. space).

Example 1

A tapped tuning fork with a frequency of 480Hz produces sound waves of wavelength 70cm. What is the speed of the sound wave?

Wave speed = Frequency × Wavelength
= 480Hz × 0.7m
= **336m/s**

Remember to calculate using the correct units

HT Example 2

Radio 5 Live transmits on a frequency of 909kHz. If the speed of radio waves is 300 000 000m/s, on what wavelength does it transmit?

$$\text{Wavelength} = \frac{\text{Wave speed}}{\text{Frequency}}$$

$$= \frac{300\,000\,000\text{m/s}}{909\,000\text{Hz}}$$

= **330m**

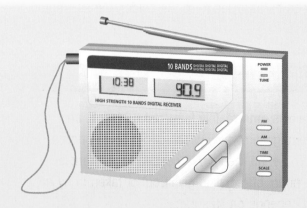

Transverse wave • Electromagnetic • Speed

Reflection

Light or another electromagnetic wave can be **reflected** from multiple surfaces, as shown in the diagram.

Refraction

A wave will speed up or slow down as it passes from one medium (material) into another. This can cause the wave to change direction and is known as **refraction**.

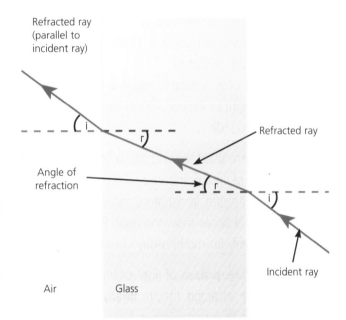

Refracted ray (parallel to incident ray)

Refracted ray

Angle of refraction

Incident ray

Air   Glass

Quick Test

1. What is meant by the 'frequency of a wave'?
2. Name two electromagnetic waves with a shorter wavelength than visible light.
3. HT State the condition needed for maximum diffraction.

Diffraction

As waves pass through a gap or an opening (such as a door), the edges spread out. This is **diffraction**.

Gap larger than wavelength – slight diffraction

HT Maximum diffraction occurs when the gap is the same width as the wavelength of the wave passing through it. This phenomenon limits the resolution and quality of the image produced by telescopes and optical microscopes. As light passes between two neighbouring particles, it is diffracted.

The intensity of the image is reduced. The light may also interfere with other diffracted light waves, distorting the image further.

Gap same size as wavelength – increased diffraction

P1 Light and Lasers

Reflection and Refraction

Light and infrared rays can be **reflected** or **refracted** when they cross a glass–air boundary. It depends on the **angle of incidence** (the angle at which they hit the boundary):

1 If the **angle of incidence** is **below** the critical angle, the light or infrared is **refracted** away from the normal.

2 If the **angle of incidence** is **above** the **critical angle**, the light or infrared is totally internally reflected and not refracted. This is known as **total internal reflection**.

3 If the **angle of incidence** is **equal to** the **critical angle**, the light or infrared travels along the glass–air boundary.

Optical fibres are used to send information in the form of pulses of light or infrared radiation. An optical fibre is a long, flexible, transparent cable of very small diameter. Optical fibres allow the rapid transmission of data necessary for modern-day communications.

In an optical fibre, **pulses** of light or infrared radiation aren't refracted: they're **totally internally reflected** along its length. This is because the glass–air boundary acts like a plane mirror.

Total internal reflection also occurs at water–air and Perspex–air boundaries.

Light is transmitted down a fibre optic cable by total internal reflection.

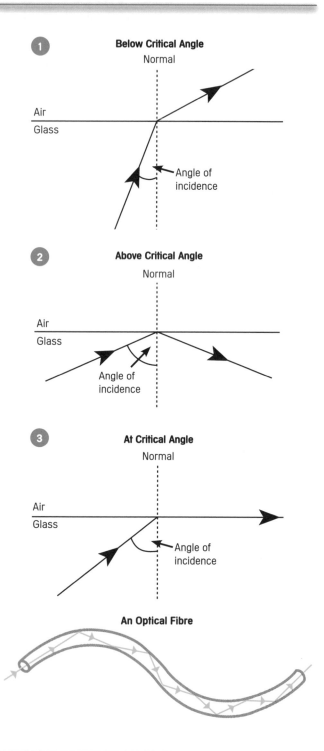

1 Below Critical Angle
Normal
Air
Glass
Angle of incidence

2 Above Critical Angle
Normal
Air
Glass
Angle of incidence

3 At Critical Angle
Normal
Air
Glass
Angle of incidence

An Optical Fibre

Wireless Signals

Electromagnetic radiation (e.g. microwaves) can be used to **send information** without optical fibres because it can be **reflected** and **refracted** in the same way as visible light. This is why it is known as **wireless technology**.

Wireless technology is used in radios, mobile phones and laptop computers. It has three main advantages:

- Signals are available 24 hours a day.
- No wiring is needed.
- Items can be portable and convenient.

Critical angle • Total internal reflection

Communication Signals

At the beginning of the last century, **Morse code** was used to communicate over long distances. This code uses long and short flashes of light to represent letters.

Like all electromagnetic waves, light travels very fast. This is why modern technology uses light as its signal.

Light used for communication is produced by a **laser**. A laser produces a narrow, intense beam of light.

Optical fibres are used to carry signals in **binary** **code** (digital signals).

(HT) This table lists the advantages and disadvantages of using various signals to send information:

Signal	Advantages	Disadvantages
Light	• Travels very fast • Small loss of signal	• Can't be used for wireless signalling as it doesn't diffract well
Electrical	• Can be sent along wires	• Signal deteriorates
Radio waves	• Can be used for wireless signalling as the waves can diffract around obstacles	• Diffraction leads to signal loss

Morse code is a digital signal because the light is either **on** or **off**.

Lasers

A **laser** produces a narrow beam of monochromatic (single colour) light.

Some uses of lasers include surgery and dental treatment, cutting materials in industry, weapon guidance and laser light shows.

(HT) **Lasers** produce a beam of light in which all light waves:

* have the same frequency
* are **in phase** with each other
* have low divergence.

Example

1. The bottom surface of a CD contains billions of tiny bumps (called pits).
2. The pits store information digitally.
3. When a CD spins, laser light is reflected by the pits.
4. The reflected pulses of light are turned into electrical signals on their way to the amplifier.

'**In phase**' means all the peaks and troughs match up, i.e. they go up together and down together:

* Waves **in phase** transfer a lot of energy.
* Waves **out of phase** transfer less overall energy.

Waves in Phase

Waves out of Phase

P1 Cooking and Communicating using Waves

Electromagnetic Radiation

The amount of radiation (such as infrared) that is absorbed or emitted from a surface depends on:

- surface temperature
- colour – black is good, white and silver are poor
- texture – dull is good, shiny is poor.

Uses of Electromagnetic Radiation

Electromagnetic radiations have many uses.

Microwaves are used to heat materials, as well as for satellite communication, mobile phones and radar. They:

- are **absorbed** by water and fat molecules, which causes them to heat up
- can **penetrate** about 1cm into food
- can cause burns when absorbed by body tissue
- can **travel** through glass and plastics
- are reflected by shiny metal surfaces.

Infrared rays are used to heat materials (in cooking), and in remote controls. They are:

- used to **heat** the surface of the food in cooking
- **reflected** off shiny surfaces
- **absorbed** by black objects.

HT Transferring Energy

Microwaves and infrared energy are transferred to materials in different ways.

Microwaves are absorbed by water and fat molecules in the outside layers of the food, increasing the kinetic energy of the particles. Energy is then transferred to the centre of the food by **conduction** or **convection**.

Infrared is absorbed by all of the particles on the surface of the food, increasing the kinetic energy of the particles. Energy is then transferred to the centre of the food by **conduction** or **convection**.

The amount of energy a microwave or an infrared wave has depends on its frequency, and this determines how potentially dangerous it could be.

Microwaves

Microwaves are used to **transmit information** over large distances that are in **line of sight**. Some areas aren't in line of sight so they have **poor signals**, which is why your mobile phone may cut out or fail to get a connection in certain areas.

The microwave signals that mobile phones use aren't the same wavelength as the microwaves used in microwave ovens.

Microwaves (Cont.)

There are some concerns that microwaves emitted by mobile phones could have a **harmful effect**. For example, microwaves *could* cause ear or brain tumours, brain damage or changes to DNA.

If using mobile phones affects people's health, then children could be more at risk from the microwave signals because their skulls are very thin. The potential risk is increased if the mobile phone is used more frequently.

There is also public concern about mobile phone transmission masts and the possible dangers to people who live near them.

Scientists publish studies into the effects of microwave radiation from mobile phones and mobile phone transmission masts. This enables other scientists to share their studies and check data from other studies.

(HT) Sometimes scientists publish conflicting evidence about studies such as mobile phone safety. In such cases, society must make choices (by balancing risk and benefit) about their own mobile phone use and/or whether to live near to a mobile phone mast.

Microwave Signals

Microwave signals can be lost or affected by:
- large obstacles such as trees or mountains, which block the signal. Microwaves are not diffracted around large objects
- poor weather conditions and large areas of surface water
- the curvature of the Earth
- **interference** between signals.

Some of the problems can be reduced by:
- limiting the distance between transmitters
- positioning masts high on top of hills and/or tall buildings.

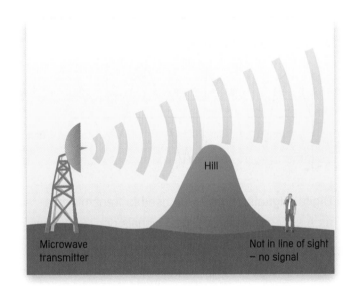

Hill

Microwave transmitter

Not in line of sight – no signal

Quick Test

1. Other than heating food, state two uses of microwaves.
2. What type of molecules in foods absorb microwaves?
3. What happens to light when it hits a glass–air boundary at an angle above the critical angle of substance?

P1 Data Transmission

Infrared Signals

Infrared radiation is a type of electromagnetic wave.

Infrared is used in many commonplace devices, for example:

- remote controls for your television and video
- sensors that control automatic doors in shops
- short-distance wireless data links for computers or mobile phones
- burglar alarms (by detecting body heat)
- security lights (by detecting body heat).

The infrared signal from a TV remote control uses digital codes to control the different functions of the TV. Each function has a different code. When a button is pressed the code is transmitted to the TV as a series of flashes.

An example of these codes might be:

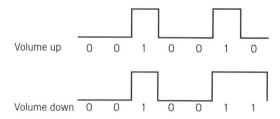

Volume up   0   0   1   0   0   1   0

Volume down   0   0   1   0   0   1   1

Analogue and Digital Signals

Analogue signals can be used to transmit data. They **vary continuously** in amplitude.

Analogue signals can have **any value** within a fixed range of values and are very similar to the sound waves of speech or music.

Digital signals can also be used to transmit data as a series of **pulses**. Digital signals don't vary; they only have **two states** – on (1) and off (0). There are no values in between.

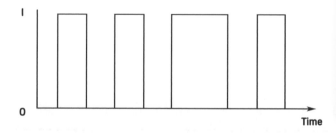

(HT) Two or more digital signals can be sent down the same **optical fibre** at the same time. This enables more information to be sent in one go, and is known as multiplexing.

Both digital and analogue signals suffer from **interference** in the form of noise. But interference doesn't affect digital signals because the signal is still only on or off. The information is in the pulse pattern (length of the on and off sections).

Analogue Signal – poor signal quality due to interference

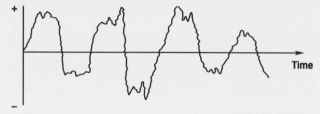

Digital Signal – high signal quality as interference is easily removed

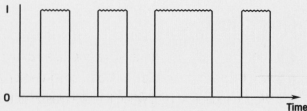

Key Words   Analogue • Amplitude • Digital • Multiplexing

Radiation for Communication

Radiation used for communication can be reflected by the atmosphere. This allows broadcasts from the south coast of England to be received in France (around the curve of the Earth). Radio stations and other nearby broadcasters must transmit using different **frequencies** to avoid interference.

Wireless technology is used for TV and radio broadcasts, mobile phones and laptops (wireless internet). Advantages and disadvantages of wireless communication are shown in the table.

Advantages
• No connection to a phone land-line required.
• Portable, convenient, allows access anywhere.

Disadvantage
• Aerial is needed to pick up the signal.

HT Transmitting Signals

Satellites can be used for **global communication**. A signal is sent from a ground station transmitter dish to a satellite receiver dish. A return signal is then sent by the satellite transmitter to a ground receiver dish, which may be in a different country, continent, etc.

The **ionosphere** is an electrically charged layer in the Earth's upper atmosphere. Longer wavelength radio waves are **reflected** by the ionosphere. This enables radio and television programmes to be transmitted between different places.

The **refraction** and **diffraction** of radiation, e.g. microwaves, can affect communications.

Refraction at the interfaces of different layers of the Earth's atmosphere results in the waves **changing direction**. Diffraction (changes to the direction and intensity of waves) at the edge of transmission dishes causes the waves to **spread out**, which results in **signal loss**.

Interference from similar signals limits the distance between transmitters. Positioning transmitters in high places can help to overcome the nuisance of obstacles blocking signals.

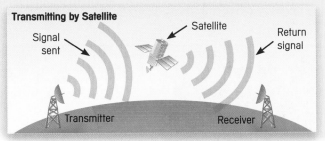

Transmitting by Satellite
Signal sent — Satellite — Return signal
Transmitter — Receiver

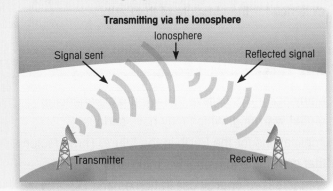

Transmitting via the Ionosphere
Ionosphere
Signal sent — Reflected signal
Transmitter — Receiver

DAB Radio

New DAB (Digital Audio Broadcasting) radios receive digital signals.

Most are also able to receive old FM radio station signals which are transmitted using analogue signals.

Advantages of DAB
• More stations are available.
• Less interference with broadcasts from other stations.

Disadvantages of DAB
• Audio quality is not as good as FM broadcasts.
• Some areas cannot receive DAB (e.g. the short wavelength signal cannot diffract around hills.

P1 Stable Earth

Earthquakes

Earthquakes produce **shock waves**, which can travel inside the Earth. They can damage buildings and cause tsunamis. These waves are called seismic waves and can be detected by **seismometers**.

There are two main types of seismic wave – **P-waves** and **S-waves**.

P-waves (primary waves) are longitudinal and travel through both solids and liquids.

S-waves (secondary waves) are transverse waves and travel through solids but not through liquids. They travel more **slowly** than P-waves.

HT Detecting Seismic Waves

After an earthquake occurs, the waves are **detected** all over the world, as shown in the diagram.

P-waves are detected in most places, so this means they can travel through the solid **crust** and **mantle**, and the liquid **outer core** and the **inner core**.

S-waves are only detected closer to the **epicentre** (the centre of the earthquake). This means they can pass through the solid **crust** and **mantle**, but they **can't** pass through the liquid outer core.

So, the properties of seismic waves provide evidence for the structure of the Earth.

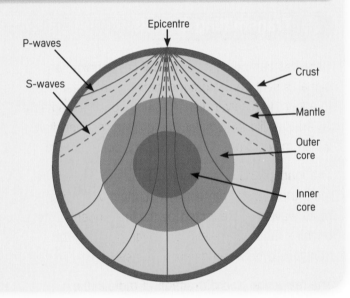

Global Warming

Many scientists believe that we are experiencing global warming, which may have serious implications for the Earth in the future. Three factors that contribute to global warming are:

- increased **energy** use in homes and industry
- increased **carbon dioxide** (CO_2) **emissions** from fossil fuels
- deforestation (the cutting down of large numbers of trees).

Weather patterns are affected by human activity, as well as by natural phenomena, for example:

- dust from volcanoes reflects radiation from the Sun back into space, causing **cooling**.
- dust from factories reflects radiation from cities back towards the Earth, causing **warming**.

Quick Test

1. Which type of seismic wave cannot travel through the liquid outer core of the Earth?
2. Deforestation contributes to global warming. True or false?

Key Words Seismic wave • Longitudinal wave • Transverse wave • Global warming • Deforestation

Dangerous Sun

The Sun produces **electromagnetic waves**, including **ultraviolet** radiation. Prolonged exposure to ultraviolet radiation can cause a sun tan, sun burn, cataracts, premature ageing and skin cancer.

Sunscreen can be effective at **reducing** the **damage** caused by ultraviolet radiation. The higher the **factor**, the lower the **risk** because high factors allow longer exposure without burning. On a bright, sunny day in England you should spend no more than 20 minutes in the sun without sun protection. The factor of sunscreen you put on increases the amount of time you can safely stay in the sun for, e.g. wearing a factor 30 sunscreen means you can stay in the sun for 30 times longer than if you had no sunscreen on: 20 mins × 30 = 600 mins = **10 hours**. But you must keep reapplying it!

People who have darker skin tones have a reduced risk of developing skin cancer. Skin cancer develops in the delicate tissues below the melanin in the skin. Melanin is the chemical which gives skin its colour. Dark skin absorbs more ultraviolet radiation than light skin. Less ultraviolet radiation reaches the underlying body tissues.

Public health campaigns have informed people about the risks of ultraviolet rays. They use a range of media in the campaigns: TV adverts, leaflets, newspapers, internet campaigns.

To reduce the risk of sunburn and developing skin cancer:

- stay out of the midday sun
- keep skin covered (wear long sleeves and a hat)
- reduce or avoid use of sun beds
- always use sun block or sunscreen.

The Ozone Layer

(HT) **Ozone** is a gas found naturally high up in the Earth's **atmosphere**, which **prevents** too many harmful **ultraviolet** (UV) rays reaching the Earth.

Recently, scientists have noticed a link between the decreasing thickness of the ozone layer and the number of people suffering from skin cancer.

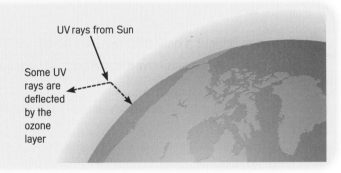

UV rays from Sun

Some UV rays are deflected by the ozone layer

Scientists who study the ozone layer must make sure their data is accurate. In order to do so, they:
- repeat their experiments using new equipment
- consider data from other scientists who replicated their experiments
- test their predictions based on current explanations.

(HT) The discovery of the hole in the ozone layer over Antarctica had an impact globally:
- Legislation was passed in many countries to ban the use of CFCs in fridge cooling systems.
- Old fridges and freezers containing CFCs must be disposed of according to strict guidelines.

- CFCs are no longer used as propellants in aerosol cans (e.g. hairspray and deodorant).

The discovery also raised a greater awareness of the risk of ultraviolet radiation and its link to sun burn and skin cancer.

1 Naz eats an ice cream in the sun. The graph shows the change in temperature of the ice cream.

a) Explain what is happening at point B. **[1]**

....

....

b) Explain what is meant by **specific heat capacity.** **[1]**

....

c) The mass of Naz's ice cream is 63g and the specific heat capacity is 1.67kJ/kg°C. Use this information and the graph above to calculate the energy transferred to the ice cream before point A. **[2]**

....

....

2 Calculate the efficiency of a light bulb that uses 100 joules of energy every second to produce 20 joules of light energy. **[2]**

....

....

3 Claire has bought a new microwave oven as she finds microwaves easy to use and convenient for cooking. Briefly explain how microwaves are used to heat food. **[4]**

....

....

....

4 Name the parts of the wave labelled on the diagram. **[4]**

A ....

B ....

C ....

D ....

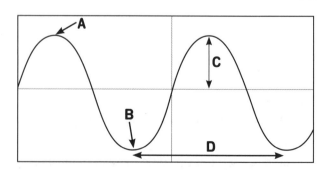

5 A radio station transmits at a frequency of 890 000Hz. The wavelength of the wave is 337m. Calculate the speed of the electromagnetic wave. **[2]**

6 a) What are the two main types of seismic wave called? .... **[1]**

b) Which of the waves named in part (a) cannot pass through the liquid part of the core? **[1]**

7 Bartez starts to burn if he stays out in the sun for 6 minutes. He applies a sun cream with SPF 20 Calculate how long he can now stay in the sun for before burning. **[2]**

8 John wants to insulate his house. He has gathered data about the different types of domestic insulation available, shown in the table.

a) Fill in the spaces in the 'Payback Time' column. **[3]**

Insulation Type	Cost	Annual Saving	Payback Time
Cavity Wall Insulation	£500	£25	
Double Glazing	£2100	£70	
Draft Excluders	£30	£20	

b) Using the data in the table, suggest which type of insulation John should choose. Explain your answer. **[1]**

HT c) John puts shiny foil behind the radiators in his house. Explain how this helps to reduce his energy bills. **[4]**

P2 Collecting Energy from the Sun

Energy from the Sun

The Sun is a stable **source** of **energy**. It emits and transfers energy to Earth as **light** and **heat**. Energy from the Sun can be captured and used to produce **electricity** and heat.

Energy from the Sun is known as **renewable** energy because it will not run out.

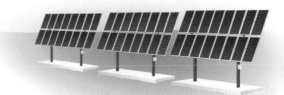

Photocells

Photocells capture light energy from the Sun on flat silicon surfaces. The light energy is then **transformed** into an **electric current** which travels in the same direction all the time. This type of electric current is known as **direct current** (**DC**).

The **power** output of a photocell depends on the surface **area** exposed to the sunlight. Lots of photocells can be joined together (as a **solar panel**) to create a larger surface area. This increases the amount of light captured from the Sun.

Some advantages and disadvantages of photocells are listed in this table.

Advantages

- They use renewable energy from the Sun.
- No need for fuel (the Sun is the energy source).
- No pollution or waste is produced.
- Little maintenance is required once they are installed.
- Have a long life.
- Can operate in remote locations to give access to electricity without installing power cables.

Disadvantages

- No power at night or during bad weather.
- Expensive to buy.
- Take up a lot of space.

HT How Photocells Work

The Sun's energy is **absorbed** by the photocell, causing **electrons** to be knocked loose from the silicon atoms in the crystal. These electrons **flow** freely within the silicon. This flow of charge is called an **electric current**.

The **power** of a photocell depends on:
- the **surface area** exposed to the light
- the **intensity** of the **light** (intensity is a measure of how powerful the light energy is)
- the distance between the light source and the photocell.

To maximise power output, an efficient solar collector must **track** (follow) the position of the Sun in the sky. This requires additional technology, which increases the initial set-up cost.

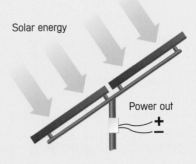

Solar energy

Power out

Energy • Renewable • Photocell • Direct current • Power

Other Uses of the Sun's Energy

Light from the Sun can be captured and used in other ways, apart from in photocells.

Light can be **absorbed** by a surface and **transformed** into heat energy. Water passes over this surface to be **heated** to a reasonable temperature. It can then be used to heat buildings.

A curved mirror can be used to **focus** the Sun's light, rather like a magnifying glass, making it more **intense**.

Buildings with a large number of windows facing the Sun can be heated by **passive solar heating**. Passive solar heating refers to a device (e.g. a greenhouse) that traps energy from the Sun but doesn't distribute the energy or change it into another form of energy. Passive solar heating causes conservatories to get hot in the summer.

Using Light to Heat Water

Flat plate collector

Hot water to house

Cold water supply

Heat exchanger

Pump

Water tank

(HT) Glass is transparent to radiation from the Sun. Passive solar heating is caused by visible light and infrared radiation passing through glass into a room. The light and infrared is **absorbed** by objects in the room, causing them to **heat up**. The objects then re-emit infrared of longer wavelength, which can't pass back through glass. Instead, it is **reflected** back into the room, causing the room to heat up.

Wind Turbines

The Sun's energy also produces **convection currents** in the air (i.e. wind). Wind turbines transform the **kinetic energy** of the air into **electrical energy**.

The advantages and disadvantages of wind turbines are listed in this table:

Advantages
• Wind is a renewable energy source.
• There is no chemical pollution or waste.
• It is free – after set-up costs.

Disadvantages
• Turbines require a large amount of space to deliver a reasonable amount of electricity.
• They are dependent on the wind (unreliable).
• Turbines cause visual pollution.

P2 Generating Electricity

The Dynamo Effect

The **dynamo effect** refers to the way in which **electricity** can be generated by:

- moving a **wire**, or a coil of wire, near a **magnet**
- moving a magnet near a wire, or coil of wire.

When this happens, the wire cuts through the lines of force of the **magnetic field** and a **current** is **produced** by **electromagnetic induction** in the wire (as long as it's part of a complete **circuit**).

The current generated can be **increased** by:

- using **stronger** magnets
- using **more turns** in the coil
- moving the **coil faster**
- moving the **magnet faster**.

Moving the Magnet Towards the Coil of Wire

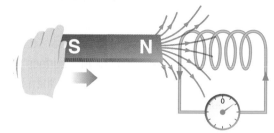

Moving the Coil of Wire Towards the Magnet

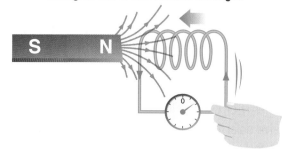

The AC Generator

In a **generator**, a coil of wire is **rotated** in a magnetic field. The coil and field should be close together.

As the coil cuts through the magnetic field, the **relative motion** causes a current to be generated in the coil.

The current **alternates**, i.e. it reverses its direction of flow, every half turn of the coil so a generator produces an **alternating current** (**AC**). This is different from a battery, which produces a **direct current** (**DC**).

The graph alongside shows an alternating current. As time passes, the line curves up into the positive area above the x-axis, and down into the negative area under the x-axis. This shows that the current alternates from a positive direction to a negative direction and back again.

The **frequency** of AC electricity is the number of **cycles** that are completed every second. For example, in the graph, it takes 4 seconds for one cycle, so the frequency is 0.25 cycles per second (1 cycle ÷ 4 seconds = 0.25Hz).

Generator

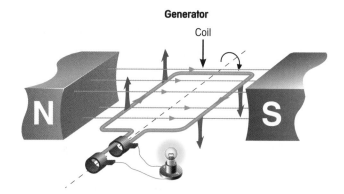

Alternating Current

Key Words　　Dynamo effect • Magnetic field • Current • Alternating current • Direct current

Producing Electricity

Electricity is produced in **power stations**:

1. The fuel (energy source) is **burned** to release heat energy.
2. The heat boils water to produce **steam**.
3. The steam drives the **turbines**, which drive **generators**.
4. The generators produce **electricity**.

The electricity produced in power stations is distributed around the country by a network of power lines called the **National Grid**. It is distributed to consumers, e.g. homes, businesses, factories, offices and farms.

A significant amount of the energy produced by conventional power stations is **wasted**.

At each stage in the electricity transfer process, energy is transferred to the **surroundings** in a 'non-useful' form, usually as **heat**.

The energy transfer diagram for the process shows how much energy is wasted at each stage. The overall efficiency is only 30%.

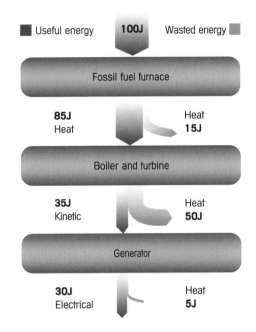

Efficiency of a Power Station

You can use the following equation to calculate the **efficiency** of a power station:

$$\text{Efficiency} = \frac{\text{Electrical energy output (J)}}{\text{Fuel energy input (J)}} \ (\times \ 100)$$

Example

A power station uses 200 000J of fuel energy to produce 80 000J of electrical energy.

What is the efficiency of the power station?

$$\text{Efficiency} = \frac{\text{Electrical energy output}}{\text{Fuel energy input}} \ (\times \ 100)$$

$$= \frac{80\,000J}{200\,000J} \ (\times \ 100) = \textbf{0.4 or 40\%}$$

Remember, answers can be left as a ratio.

P2 Global Warming

Global Warming

Many **greenhouse gases** occur naturally.
Greenhouse gases in the atmosphere trap heat and warm the Earth sufficiently to support life.

Over the past 50 years, scientists have collected data that suggests that the temperature of the Earth is increasing. This is called **global warming**.

Most electromagnetic radiation from the Sun can pass through the Earth's atmosphere.
Some wavelengths are absorbed by the gases in the atmosphere. This prevents heat radiating into space.

Greenhouse gases include:

- carbon dioxide
- water vapour
- methane.

These gases are produced when fuels are burned.

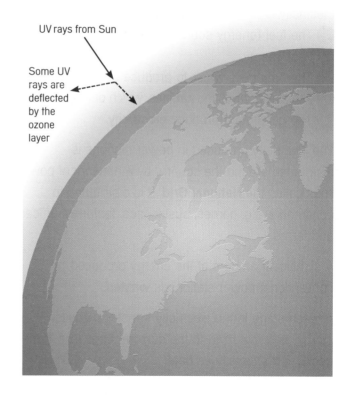

UV rays from Sun

Some UV rays are deflected by the ozone layer

Causes of Global Warming

Although many scientists agree that the average temperature of the atmosphere is increasing, they disagree about why it's happening.

Some believe that the Earth is following a natural cycle, whilst others believe that man's activity on Earth (burning fossil fuels and increased industry) is to blame.

Causes of Global Warming (Cont.)

The table below shows evidence which supports manmade global warming and evidence which refutes (disagrees with) it.

Supports	Refutes
• Humans are burning more fossil fuels. • The amount of carbon dioxide in the atmosphere is increasing. • Greenhouse gases trap heat and prevent it from escaping into space. • The average temperature of the planet is increasing.	• The temperature of the Earth changes over time (increasing and decreasing in a 40 000 year cycle). • The increase in carbon dioxide in the atmosphere is not significant enough to affect global temperatures. • Water vapour has a much more significant effect on global warming. • The surface temperatures of Mercury and Venus have increased, which isn't due to humans.

Some statements are **evidence-based**. This means that they're based upon data gathered from scientific experiments, or on data collated from previous studies. Some statements are **opinion-based**. This means that they haven't been tested scientifically.

Scientists may agree that the average temperature of the Earth has increased, but still disagree as to the cause.

More studies may be needed to determine whether global warming is due to human activity. Before data is universally accepted, it must be **repeatable** by other scientists, and **verified** as **accurate**.

HT The Greenhouse Effect

The greenhouse effect occurs because short wavelength electromagnetic radiation from the Sun is absorbed by the Earth, causing it to heat up. The Earth then radiates heat as **longer wavelength** infrared radiation. Greenhouse gases absorb some of these longer wavelength infrared waves, warming the atmosphere.

Quick Test

1. What is meant by the term 'renewable energy'?
2. What are the three factors that affect the power output of a photocell?
3. What are the four stages of electricity production in a conventional power station?
4. Name two greenhouse gases.

P2 Fuels for Power

Power Station Fuels

This table shows the fuels that are commonly used in power stations:

Type of Fuel	Examples	Method of Releasing Energy
Fossil fuel	• Crude oil • Coal • Natural gas	Fuel burned to release heat energy.
Biomass	• Wood • Straw • Manure	Biomass fermented to generate methane.
Nuclear fuel	• Uranium	Fuel rods release heat energy.

Distributing Electricity

The electricity produced in power stations is distributed around the country by a network of power lines called the **National Grid**. The electricity has to be transmitted at very high voltage (about 40 000V) to reduce heat loss and costs.

Transformers are used to increase and decrease the voltage before and after transmission. The voltage is too high for use by consumers so **transformers** are used to reduce the voltage for safe use. A transformer that does this is called a **step-down transformer**.

(HT) As an electric current is transmitted along a wire, the wire heats up due to collisions within the material. The wire loses this heat to the environment.

If the electricity is transmitted at a higher voltage (but the power remains the same), the current in the wire is reduced. A lower current means less heating of the wires, so less energy lost from the wires as heat.

(HT) Off-Peak Electricity

There is a lower demand for electricity at night because most people are asleep.

To encourage consumers to use electricity during the night-time period, electricity companies offer an off-peak rate for 7 hours every night, which is called **Economy-7**.

The advantages and disadvantage of Economy-7 are listed in the table.

Advantages
• Less demand for electricity at night.
• Cheaper electricity for the consumer.
• Avoids wasting electrical energy.

Disadvantage
• Inconvenient to run appliances at night because of the noise they make.

HT Comparing Energy Sources

The table below lists the advantages and disadvantages of different types of fuels and renewable energy sources.

Source	Advantages	Disadvantages
Fossil fuel, e.g. coal, oil, gas	• Relatively cheap and easy to obtain. • Enough reserves for short to medium term. • Coal-, oil- and gas-fired power stations are flexible in meeting demand and have a relatively quick start-up time. • Burning gas doesn't produce SO_2.	• Burning produces CO_2 which causes global warming, and SO_2 (except burning gas) which causes acid rain. • Removing SO_2 from waste gases (to reduce global warming) adds to the cost. • Oil is often carried between continents in tankers, leading to risk of spillage and pollution. • Expensive pipelines and networks are often required to transport it to the point of use.
Biomass, e.g. wood, straw, manure	• It is renewable.	• Produces CO_2 and SO_2 which damage the environment. • Large area is needed to grow trees, which could be used for other purposes, e.g. growing food.
Nuclear fuel, e.g. uranium	• Cost and rate of fuel production is relatively low. • Can be situated in sparsely populated areas. • Nuclear power stations are flexible in meeting demand. • Doesn't produce CO_2 or SO_2 (greenhouse gases). • High stocks of nuclear fuel. • Can reduce use of fossil fuels.	• Radioactive material can stay dangerously radioactive for thousands of years and can be harmful. • Storing radioactive waste is very expensive. • Building and decommissioning nuclear power stations are costly processes. • Comparatively long start-up time. • Risk of accidental release of radioactive material. • High maintenance costs.
Renewable sources, e.g. wind, tidal, hydroelectric, solar	• Produce clean electricity. • Can be constructed in remote areas. • No fuel costs during operation. • No chemical pollution. • Often low maintenance. • Don't contribute to global warming or produce acid rain once set up.	• With the exception of hydroelectric, they produce small amounts of electricity. • Take up lots of space and are unsightly. • Unreliable (apart from hydroelectric), dependent on the weather and cannot guarantee supply on demand. • High initial capital outlay.

P2 Fuels for Power

Power

An **electric current** is the flow of electric charge from the battery (or other power supply) to the components in the circuit. The components then **transfer** the energy, for example, a lamp changes electrical energy into light energy.

The **rate** of the **energy transfer** determines the **power** of the component or device and is measured in:

- joules per second (J/s)
- **watts** (W) – 1 watt is the transfer of 1 joule of energy in 1 second.
- kilowatts (kW) – 1kW is the same as 1000W.

You can calculate the **power** of an appliance using this formula:

$$\text{Power (W)} \ = \ \text{Current (A)} \ \times \ \text{Voltage (V)}$$

Example

Calculate the power of a lamp when the current flowing through it is 0.3A and the voltage across it is 3V.

Power = Current × Voltage

= 0.3A × 3V

= **0.9 watts**

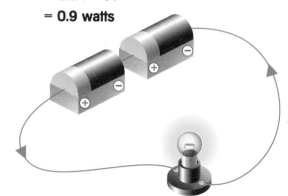

Kilowatt Hours

The power of an appliance is measured in watts (W) or kilowatts (kW). 1kW = 1000W. A **kilowatt hour** (kWh) is a measure of how much electrical energy has been used.

The number of kWh units of electricity used by an appliance depends on:

- the **power rating** (in kilowatts, kW) of the appliance
- the **time** (in hours, h) that the appliance is switched on for.

You can use the following formula to calculate the cost of using an appliance for a certain length of time:

$$\text{Total cost (p)} \ = \ \text{Number of kilowatt hours used (kWh)} \ \times \ \text{Cost per unit (p)}$$

Example

If electricity costs 8p per kWh, what is the cost of using 3kWh?

Total cost = Number of kWh used × Cost per unit

= 3kWh × 8p = **24p**

(HT) Use this formula to calculate energy supplied:

$$\text{Energy supplied (kWh)} \ = \ \text{Power (kW)} \ \times \ \text{Time (h)}$$

N.B. When doing these calculations the power needs to be in kilowatts, and the time needs to be in hours.

Example

A 1.5kW electric hot plate was switched on for 2 hours. How much electricity was supplied?

Energy supplied = Power × Time

= 1.5kW × 2h = **3kWh**

Quick Test

1. Name three types of fuel used in power stations.
2. Nuclear power is **not** a 'renewable source'. Why?
3. State the equation used to calculate electrical power.

Background Radiation

Radioactive **materials** are substances that give out nuclear **radiation** all the time. Radioactivity involves a **change** in the structure of the radioactive atom and the **release** of one or more of the three types of nuclear radiation: **alpha** (α), **beta** (β) and **gamma** (γ).

Radiation that occurs naturally all around us is called **background radiation**. It only provides a very small dose, so there is no danger to our health. Some sources of background radiation include:

- radioactive substances in rocks, soil and living things
- **cosmic rays** from outer space and the Sun.

Penetration and Ionisation

Each type of radiation has a different **penetrative** power, i.e. the different radiations can pass through different thicknesses of different materials.

Alpha, beta and gamma radiations cause **ionisation** that can **damage** 'healthy' molecules in **living cells**, resulting in the death of the cell. This can also lead to **cancer**.

People who handle radioactive materials need to take safety measures such as:

- wearing protective clothing
- keeping their distance by using tongs to hold the material whenever possible
- trying to minimise their exposure time
- storing radioactive materials in clearly labelled, **shielded** containers.

Radiation can also be beneficial.

Particle	Ionising Power	Penetrating Power
Alpha	Strong	Absorbed by a few centimetres of air or thin paper.
Beta	Reasonable	Passes through air and paper. Absorbed by a few millimetres of aluminium.
Gamma	Weak	Very penetrating. Needs many centimetres of lead or metres of concrete to stop it.

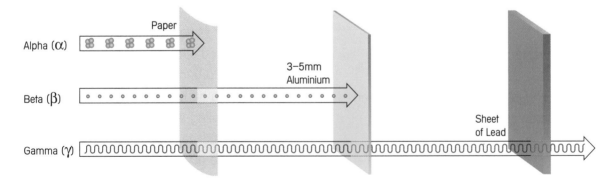

You can identify whether radiation is alpha, beta or gamma by finding out what material it can penetrate.

During ionisation, a particle gains or loses electrons, leaving the atom charged. A gain in electrons gives a negative ion and if the atom loses electrons it becomes a positive ion.

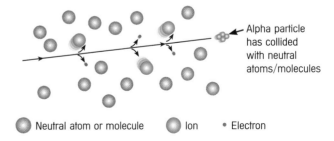

Alpha particle has collided with neutral atoms/molecules

○ Neutral atom or molecule   ○ Ion   • Electron

P2 Nuclear Radiations

Use of Alpha Radiation

Most **smoke detectors** contain Americium-241, which emits alpha **radiation**. The emitted alpha particles **ionise** air particles and the **ions** formed are **attracted** to the oppositely charged **electrodes**. This produces a **current** in the circuit.

When smoke enters the space between the two electrodes, less ionisation takes place as the alpha particles are absorbed by the smoke particles. A smaller current then flows, which triggers an alarm.

Uses of Beta Radiation

A **tracer** is a small amount of a **radioactive substance** that is put into a system so that its progress through the system can be followed using a radiation detector.

A beta emitter tracer can be used to observe how elements such as nitrogen and phosphorus move through a plant, from root to leaf.

Beta radiation is used in a **paper thickness gauge**. When beta radiation passes through the paper, some of it is absorbed. If the paper thickness is too great, more beta radiation is absorbed and less passes through to the detector. This indicates that the thickness of the paper needs to be reduced.

Uses of Gamma Radiation

Gamma radiation can be used to **treat cancer** because it destroys cancerous cells. But care must be taken not to destroy the healthy cells. It can also be used to **sterilise medical equipment** because it can destroy microorganisms like bacteria.

Non-destructive **tests** can be carried out on welds using gamma radiation, by placing a gamma source on one side of the material. Any cracks or defects are then identified using a detector (e.g. photographic film) on the other side.

Dealing with Radioactive Waste

Spent fuel is taken to be **reprocessed** – the unused fuel and plutonium are removed. The rest is **disposed** of:

- Low-level waste is sealed and buried in landfill sites.
- Higher-level waste is enclosed in glass and stored underground in steel cylinders.

(HT) There are four main **problems** to bear in mind when dealing with radioactive waste:

- It remains radioactive for a long time and must be disposed of safely.
- It may be a target for terrorist activity.
- It needs to be kept out of ground water to avoid contaminating drinking supplies.
- The level of radioactivity that's deemed to be acceptable may change over time, so measures may need to be modified.

Quick Test

1. Which type of radiation is the most penetrating?
2. Give two uses of gamma radiation.
3. How is high-level radioactive waste stored?

Ion • Current • Tracer

The Universe

The Universe is made up of:

- **planets**, **comets** and **meteors**
- **stars**, e.g. our Sun – they can be clearly seen even though they are far away because they are very hot and give out light
- **galaxies** – large groups of stars
- **black holes** – dense, dying stars with a strong gravitational field.

(HT) Black holes can be found throughout the Universe and in every galaxy. They have a **very large mass** concentrated into a **very small space**. This means that their **gravity** is very **large**; this is why nothing can escape from black holes – not even light.

Orbits in the Solar System

The Sun is in the centre of our Solar System. The eight planets (including Earth) and comets move around the Sun in slightly squashed circles (ellipses) called **orbits**.

Satellites orbit planets. The moon is a satellite that is in orbit around the Earth.

Planets, comets and satellites are kept in their orbits by the **gravitational force** of the larger object they are orbiting.

(HT) The planets, comets and satellites travel in circular (or near circular) paths around a larger object. They stay in their orbits because the larger object exerts an **inward pull force** on them.

This inward pull force is provided by **gravity** and is called the **centripetal force**, e.g. the Earth orbits the Sun because of the gravitational pull force of the Sun.

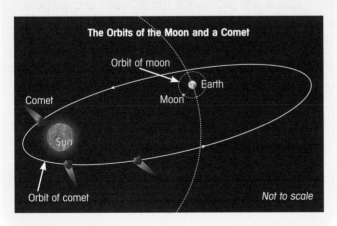

The Orbits of the Moon and a Comet

Orbit of moon

Earth

Comet

Moon

Sun

Orbit of comet

Not to scale

The Sun and the Planets in the Solar System

Sun

Mercury

Venus

Earth

Mars

Jupiter

Saturn

Uranus

Neptune

Pluto

Not to scale

N.B. Pluto has been known as a dwarf planet since September 2006.

P2 Exploring Our Solar System

Manned Space Travel

Space is a very dangerous place. There are many **difficulties** which face a **manned** space mission to the planets.

Here are some problems with manned space missions:

- The planets are very, very far away so it can take months or years to reach them.
- The fuel required takes up most of the spacecraft.

- Room must be found to store enough food, water and oxygen for the whole journey.
- A stable artificial atmosphere must be maintained in the spacecraft.
- The temperature in space is freezing, so keeping warm is vitally important.
- Outside of the Earth's magnetic field, humans need shielding from cosmic rays.
- The low **gravity** affects people's health.
- Radio signals take a very long time to reach the Earth!

Unmanned Space Travel

A far more safe and realistic option is to explore our Solar System using **unmanned** spacecraft.

As well as being able to withstand conditions that are lethal to humans, these probes don't require food, water or oxygen.

Once they arrive on a planet, probes can be used to send back information about the planet's:

- temperature
- magnetic field
- radiation levels
- gravity
- atmosphere
- surrounding landscape.

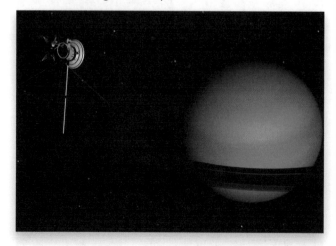

Samples from nearby (the moon) can be brought back to Earth for analysis.

(HT) Once a probe arrives on a planet, it can send information to Earth through radio waves which travel at the speed of light. The distance light travels in a year is called a light year. This measurement is used when talking about **very large distances**.

This table lists the advantages and disadvantages of using unmanned spacecraft:

Advantages
• Costs are lower as there is no need to provide space and provisions (food, water and oxygen) for human passengers. • With no humans aboard, safety is no longer a consideration.

Disadvantages
• Reliability has to be high as there will be no one to fix any breakdowns. • Instruments must require zero maintenance.

Gravity • Light year

Asteroids

Asteroids are rocks left over from the formation of the Solar System. They normally **orbit** the Sun in a **belt** between Mars and Jupiter but occasionally they get knocked off course and head towards Earth.

When an asteroid **collides** with Earth there can be several devastating **consequences**:

- An impact would form a crater, which could trigger the ejection of hot rocks.
- The heat may cause widespread fires.
- Sunlight could be blocked out by the dust from an explosion (so plants wouldn't be able to photosynthesise).
- It could trigger a climate change.
- Whole species could become extinct.

There is evidence to suggest that asteroids have collided with Earth many times in the past:

- Craters can be found all over the planet.
- There are layers of unusual elements found in rocks.
- There are sudden changes in the number of fossils found in adjacent rock layers, which could be due to the sudden death of many animals.

(HT) When asteroids in the belt of asteroids between Jupiter and Mars bump into each other they can join up or shatter. They can't combine to form a new planet because the larger mass formed feels a greater pull from Jupiter's strong gravitational field and is attracted to it and breaks up.

Comets

A **comet** is a small body with a core of frozen gas (ice) and dust. The characteristic tail is a trail of debris. Comets come from the objects that orbit the Sun. Comets have **highly elliptical orbits** around the Sun. The **speed** of the comet **increases** as it approaches the Sun.

(HT) The comet's speed increases as a result of the increase in the strength of **gravity** as it approaches the star (Sun). It can also be affected by the gravity of planets.

Near Earth Objects (NEOs)

A **Near Earth Object** is an asteroid or comet that is on a possible collision course with Earth.

Telescopes are used to observe these objects in an attempt to determine their **trajectories** (probable paths).

(HT) Large NEOs may pose a threat to the human race, but there are actions we can take to reduce the threat:

- Survey the skies with telescopes to identify likely NEOs as early as possible.
- Monitor the object's progress with satellites.
- Deflect the object with an explosion if a collision is likely (as long as it isn't too close to Earth).

The Moon

The moon may be the remains of a planet which collided with the Earth billions of years ago. A collision between two planets could result in an Earth–moon system in this way:

- The planets collide.

- The iron cores of each planet merge to form the core of the Earth.
- Less dense material becomes the moon and begins to orbit the Earth.

P2 The Big Bang

Big Bang Theory

The **Big Bang theory** can be used to explain how the Universe arrived at its present state. The theory states:

- the Universe started **billions of years ago** in one place with a huge explosion, i.e. a **big bang**
- the Universe is **expanding**.

When we look at the stars we can observe that:

- nearly all the galaxies are moving away from us
- distant galaxies are moving away more quickly
- microwave radiation is received from all parts of the Universe.

(HT) Red shift is the shifting of the wavelengths of light towards the red end of the spectrum. It can be observed in the light we receive from galaxies. The further away a galaxy is, the greater the red shift. This means that galaxies further away from us are travelling faster than those closer to us.

Measuring red shift provides **evidence** for the expansion of the Universe. By tracking the movement of the galaxies, we can **estimate** the age and starting point of the Universe.

The Life of a Star

(HT) A **proto-star** is formed when interstellar gas clouds collapse under gravitational attraction. Then thermonuclear fusion reactions take place, releasing massive amounts of energy and increasing the star's temperature. During this time, the star experiences a long period of normal life (**main sequence**). But, eventually, the supply of hydrogen runs out, causing the end of the star. The type of end depends largely on the **mass** of the star.

End Stages of a Heavy-Weight Star

Star → Red supergiant → Supernova → Neutron star, Black hole

End Stages of a Medium-Weight Star

Star → Red giant → Planetary nebula → White dwarf

Stars start as huge clouds of gas. They have a **finite** (limited) life, depending on the star's supply of hydrogen. Stars are different sizes. Their size determines how they change during the end stages of their life.

End stages of a **heavy-weight star**:

1. Star swells up to form a **red supergiant**.
2. The red supergiant rapidly shrinks and explodes, releasing massive amounts of energy, dust and gas into space. This is a **supernova**.
3. The next stage depends on the size of the star:
   - The remnants of stars up to ten times the mass of our Sun form a **neutron star**, which is made of very dense matter.
   - Stars greater than ten times the mass of our Sun leave behind **black holes**. Black holes can only be observed indirectly through their effects on their surroundings – light cannot escape from a black hole because its gravitational pull is too big.

End stages of a **medium-weight star** (like our Sun):

1. Star swells up to form a **red giant**.
2. The core of the red giant contracts (shrinks) to be surrounded by outer shells of gas (**planetary nebula**).
3. The core cools and contracts to become a **white dwarf**, with a density thousands of times greater than any matter on Earth.

Key Words   **Big Bang Theory • Red Shift • Thermonuclear fusion • Red giant • White dwarf**

Models of the Universe

People haven't always believed that the Sun is the centre of our solar system, or that there is anything beyond the stars. A number of models of the Universe were put forward before the model accepted today.

The Ptolemaic Model of the Universe

The **Ptolemaic model** stated that the Earth was the centre of the Universe (the **geocentric model**) and that the Earth was surrounded by crystal spheres which held the other planets and the stars.

The Copernican Model of the Universe

The **Copernican model** was proposed in the 16th century by the astronomer **Copernicus**.
Many of its ideas were the same as the Ptolemaic model:

- The planets sat on spheres, a fixed distance from the Sun.
- The stars were fixed on the outermost sphere and didn't move.

But, the Copernican model differed from the Ptolemaic model in the following ways. It stated that:

- the Sun is the centre of the Universe
- the Earth rotated once every 24 hours
- the Earth takes one year to revolve around the Sun.

Galileo

Later in the 16th century, **Galileo** used telescopes to observe the surface of the moon. He discovered that it wasn't a perfect sphere (all heavenly bodies were thought to be perfect spheres at that time). He also discovered four moons orbiting Jupiter.

He later discovered that Venus has phases like the moon, which meant that Venus couldn't be attached to a crystal sphere, but that it orbited the Sun, like the Earth.

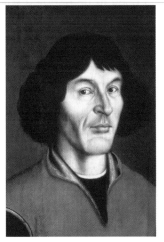

Nicolaus Copernicus   Galileo Galilei

(HT) The theories of Copernicus and Galileo were not widely accepted. Their ideas were in direct opposition to the Catholic Church's belief that the Earth was the centre of the Universe.

It took many years before Galileo's theory of the nature of the Universe was accepted.

Advances in technology, and the ability to build more powerful telescopes led to observations that supported the **heliocentric theory** (that the Sun was the centre of the Solar System).

Quick Test

1. What is an asteroid?
2. What is a comet?
3. What will a medium weight star, like our Sun, eventually become?

P2 Exam Practice Questions

1 David works for a nuclear power station. He has to work with radioactive materials on a daily basis.

   a) Radioactive materials need to be handled with care. Describe the safety precautions David must take. **[3]**

....

....

....

   b) Radiation occurs naturally all around us, but it only provides a small dose so it is harmless. Describe two sources of background radiation. **[2]**

....

....

   c) Give one use for each type of radiation. **[3]**

     i) Alpha: .... **ii)** Beta: .... **iii)** Gamma: ....

2 a) How can you generate an electric current in a wire? **[1]**

....

   b) Describe three ways to increase the current generated by the dynamo effect. **[3]**

....

....

....

3 a) A coal-fired power station provides 50 000J of electrical energy for every 150 000J of coal it burns. Calculate the efficiency of the power station. **[2]**

....

....

   b) Describe the four stages of power generation in the coal-fired power station. **[2]**

....

4 Suggest two pieces of evidence that show that asteroids collided with the Earth in the past. **[2]**

5 a) A 1200W hairdryer is used for 15 minutes. How many kilowatt hours of electricity does it use? **[2]**

b) An oven uses 3kWh of energy during a 2 hour period. What is its power rating? **[2]**

6 Describe the similarities and differences between the Ptolemaic and Copernican models of the Universe. **[6]**

The quality of your written communication will be assessed in your answer to this question.

HT 7 Most asteroids are found between Mars and Jupiter. Explain why these rocks do not join together to form new planets. **[2]**

P3 Speed

Measuring Speed

The **speed** of an object is a measure of how fast it's moving. Speed is measured in:

*   metres per second (m/s)
*   kilometres per hour (km/h)
*   miles per hour (mph).

You can work out the speed of a moving object if you know:

*   the **distance** it travels (measured using a measuring tape/trundle wheel)
*   the **time it takes** to travel that distance (measured using a stopwatch/stopclock).

The faster the speed of an object:

*   the greater the distance it travels in a particular time
*   the shorter the time it takes to travel a particular distance.

You can calculate the speed of an object by using this formula:

$$\text{Speed} = \frac{\text{Distance travelled}}{\text{Time taken}} \qquad \boxed{\frac{d}{s \times t}}$$

The speed may change over a given distance so the average distance over the whole journey is used.

$$\text{Distance} = \text{Average speed} \times \text{Time} = \left(\frac{u + v}{2}\right) \times t$$

where u is initial speed and v is final speed

Example 1

Calculate the speed of a cyclist who travels 2400m in 5 minutes.

$$\text{Speed} = \frac{\text{Distance}}{\text{Time taken}}$$

$$= \frac{2400m}{300s} = \textbf{8m/s}$$

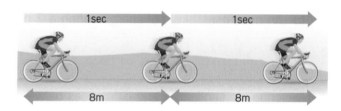

You can rearrange the speed formula to calculate either distance or time taken.

Example 2

Calculate the distance a car travels in 90 minutes if it's travelling at a constant speed of 80km/h.

$$\text{Distance} = \text{Speed} \times \text{Time taken}$$

$$= 80km/h \times 1.5h = \textbf{120km}$$

Example 3

Calculate the time it takes a motorcyclist to travel a distance of 120km at 50km/h.

$$\text{Time taken} = \frac{\text{Distance}}{\text{Speed}}$$

$$= \frac{120km}{50km/h} = 2.4 \text{ hours} = \textbf{2h 24min}$$

Speed Cameras

Speed cameras generally take **two pictures** of a vehicle a **certain amount of time apart**. The position of the vehicle in relation to the **distance markings** on the road in the two pictures can be used to calculate the vehicle's speed.

$$\text{Speed of car} = \frac{\text{Distance travelled between pictures}}{\text{Time taken between first and second picture}}$$

Distance–Time Graphs

The slope of a distance–time graph represents the **speed** of an object. The **steeper the gradient** (**slope**), the **greater the speed**.

This graph shows the movement of three people.

1. A stationary person standing 10m from point (O).
2. A person moving at a constant speed of 2m/s.
3. A person moving at a greater constant speed of 3m/s.
4. A person moving at the same speed as 2 but in the opposite direction. This graph will have the same gradient but will slope in the opposite direction.

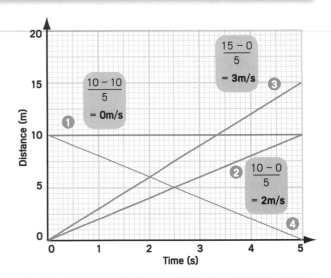

To work out the speed of an object, take any two points on a distance–time graph and read off the distance travelled for that part of the journey, and the time taken to get there (see Graph 1).

By looking at the graph, you can use the formula to calculate the speed at each part of the journey.

O to A: Speed = $\dfrac{15 - 0m}{3s}$ = **5m/s**

A to B: Speed = $\dfrac{15 - 15m}{5s}$ = **0m/s**

B to C: Speed = $\dfrac{0 - 15m}{4s}$ = **−3.75m/s** ◄ Negative sign shows that the object is moving in the reverse direction, i.e. back towards the starting point.

So, the object:
- travelled at 5m/s for 3 seconds
- remained stationary for 5 seconds
- travelled at 3.75m/s for 4 seconds back to the starting point.

Graphs can also be drawn for **non-uniform speed** (see Graph 2).

Graph 1 – Calculating Speed

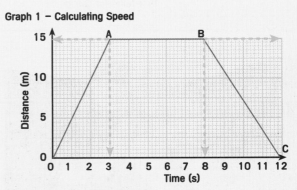

Graph 2 – Non-uniform Speed

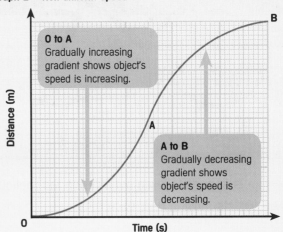

O to A
Gradually increasing gradient shows object's speed is increasing.

A to B
Gradually decreasing gradient shows object's speed is decreasing.

Quick Test

1. What two quantities are needed to calculate speed?
2. What does the gradient of a distance–time graph represent?

P3 Changing Speed

Measuring Acceleration

The **acceleration** or **deceleration** of an object is the change in **speed** per second. It's a measure of how quickly an object **speeds up** or **slows down**.

Acceleration is **only** measured in **metres per second squared** (m/s^2).

To work out the acceleration of a moving object you need to know:

- the **change in speed**
- the **time taken** for the change in speed.

You can calculate the acceleration (or deceleration) of an object by using this formula:

$$\text{Acceleration (m/s}^2\text{)} = \frac{\text{Change in speed (m/s)}}{\text{Time taken for change (s)}}$$

Example 1

A cyclist accelerates uniformly from rest and reaches a speed of 10m/s after 5 seconds. He then decelerates uniformly and comes to rest in a further 10 seconds.

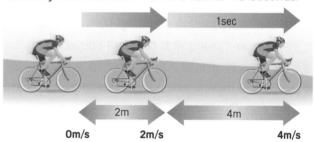

0m/s　　**2m/s**　　　　　　**4m/s**

a) Calculate his acceleration.

$$\text{Acceleration} = \frac{\text{Change in Speed}}{\text{Time taken for change}}$$

$$= \frac{10 - 0 \text{m/s}}{5\text{s}} = \textbf{2m/s}^2$$

b) Calculate his deceleration (negative acceleration).

$$= \frac{0 - 10\text{m/s}}{10\text{s}} = \textbf{-1m/s}^2 \text{ accleration}$$

$$= \textbf{1m/s}^2 \text{ deceleration}$$

HT The acceleration formula can be rearranged to calculate time taken or change in speed.

Example 2

A car accelerates at 1.5m/s^2 for 12 seconds. Calculate the change in speed of the car.

Change in speed = Acceleration × Time taken

$$= 1.5\text{m/s}^2 × 12\text{s} = \textbf{18m/s}$$

*N.B. Acceleration can involve a **change of direction** as well as **speed**. It is a **vector quantity**.*

Relative Speed

Direction is important when considering the motion of two objects moving near each other.

Example 1

Two cyclists move towards each other at speeds of 4m/s. The first cyclist sees the other cyclist moving towards him. He appears to be moving towards him at a speed of 8m/s. This is the **relative speed**.

Example 2

Two cyclists are moving in the same direction. The cyclist at the front appears to be moving away from the other cyclist at a relative speed of 2m/s, increasing the gap between them.

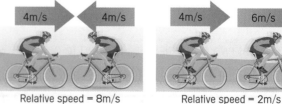

Relative speed = 8m/s　　　　Relative speed = 2m/s

Speed–Time Graphs

The slope of a **speed–time graph** represents the **acceleration** of the object. A constant acceleration increases the speed.

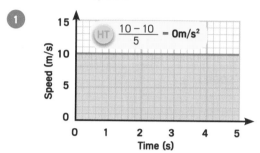

This graph shows an object moving at a constant speed of 10m/s. It **isn't** accelerating.

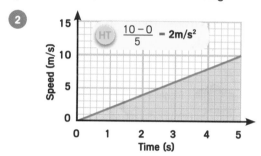

This graph shows an object moving at a constant acceleration of 2m/s².

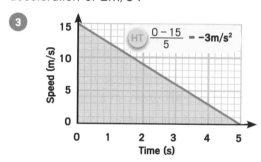

This graph shows an object moving at a constant acceleration of −3m/s².

*N.B. The **area underneath the line** in a speed–time graph represents the **total distance travelled**.*

Quick Test

1. State the equation used to calculate acceleration.
2. What does an acceleration of −5m/s² tell you about the motion of the object?

(HT) To work out the acceleration of an object, take any two points on a speed–time graph and read off the change in speed over the chosen period, and the time taken for this change.

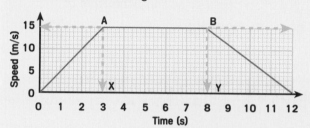

You can use the formula to calculate the acceleration at each part of the journey.

0 to A: Acceleration = $\dfrac{15\text{m/s} - 0\text{m/s}}{3\text{s}}$ = **5m/s²**

A to B: Acceleration = $\dfrac{15\text{m/s} - 15\text{m/s}}{5\text{s}}$ = **0m/s²**

B to C: Acceleration = $\dfrac{0\text{m/s} - 15\text{m/s}}{4\text{s}}$ = **-3.75m/s²**

So, the object:
- accelerated at 5m/s² for 3 seconds
- travelled at a constant speed of 15m/s for 5 seconds
- decelerated at a rate of 3.75m/s² for 4 seconds.

> The total distance travelled can be calculated by working out the area under the speed–time graph.

= Area of OAX + Area of ABYX + Area of BCY

= $(\frac{1}{2} \times 3 \times 15) + (5 \times 15) + (\frac{1}{2} \times 4 \times 15)$ = **127.5m**

Graphs can also be drawn to represent **non-uniform** motion.

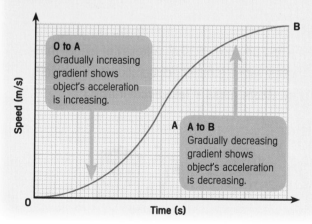

0 to A
Gradually increasing gradient shows object's acceleration is increasing.

A to B
Gradually decreasing gradient shows object's acceleration is decreasing.

Forces in Action

Forces, measured in **newtons (N)**, are **pushes** or **pulls**. They may be **different in size** and **act in different directions**.

Forces can cause objects to **accelerate** or decelerate, for example:

- **Weight** causes an apple falling from a tree to speed up as it falls.
- **Friction** causes a car to slow down.
- **Air resistance** causes a skydiver to slow down a lot when the parachute opens. If air resistance and weight are balanced, the skydiver stays at the same speed.

Force, Mass and Acceleration

If an unbalanced force acts, the acceleration of the object will depend on:

- the force applied to the object
- the **mass** of the object.

Example

A boy pushes a trolley. He exerts an unbalanced force which causes the trolley to move and accelerate.

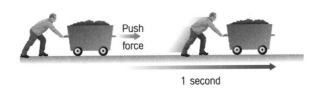

If two boys push the same trolley, it moves with a greater acceleration. (**More force = more acceleration.**)

If the first boy now pushes a trolley of bigger mass, it moves with a smaller acceleration than the first trolley. (**More mass = less acceleration.**)

If two trolleys with different masses move with a constant acceleration, the trolley with the larger mass will have to be pushed with more force than the trolley with the smaller mass. (**More mass = more force required.**)

The relationship between force, mass and acceleration is shown in this formula:

Resultant force (N)	=	Mass (kg)	×	Acceleration (m/s²)

A **newton (N)** can be defined as the force needed to give a **mass of one kilogram** an acceleration of one **metre per second per second** ($1\,m/s^2$).

Example

A trolley of mass 400kg is accelerating at $0.5\,m/s^2$. What force is needed to achieve this acceleration?

Force = Mass × Acceleration
= $400kg \times 0.5\,m/s^2$
= **200N**

Stopping Distance

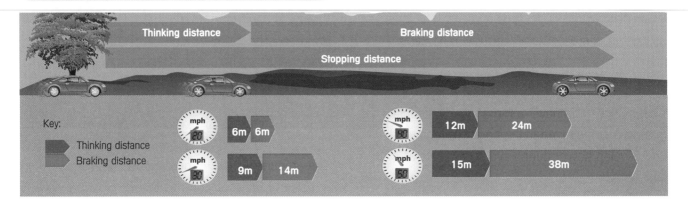

Thinking distance		Braking distance
	Stopping distance	

Key:
Thinking distance
Braking distance

mph 20	6m	6m
mph 30	9m	14m
mph 40	12m	24m
mph 50	15m	38m

Stopping distance = Thinking distance + Braking distance

The stopping distance of a vehicle depends on:
- the thinking distance – the distance travelled by the vehicle from the point the driver realises he needs to brake to when he applies the brakes
- the braking distance – the distance it takes the vehicle to stop once the driver applies the brakes.

The **thinking distance** is **increased** if:
- the vehicle is travelling faster
- the driver is ill, tired or under the influence of alcohol or drugs
- the driver is distracted or isn't concentrating.

The **braking distance** is **increased** if:
- the vehicle is travelling faster
- there is poor weather / bad road conditions, e.g. if it's wet, slippery or icy
- the vehicle is in a poor condition, e.g. worn brakes and tyres or under-inflated tyres.

The thinking distance and braking distance of a vehicle depend on the vehicle's **speed**.

It takes much longer to stop at faster speeds, so road safety regulations advise you to:
- obey the speed limits
- keep your distance from the car in front
- allow extra room between cars (or drive more slowly) in bad weather or poor road conditions.

(HT) The braking distance of a vehicle is increased if:
- the **mass** of the vehicle is **increased** – a loaded vehicle has a greater **kinetic energy**
- the **friction** between the tyres and the road is **decreased** – a wet or greasy road surface reduces the amount of friction between the tyres and the road
- the **braking force** applied is **decreased** – a smaller force is exerted by the brake pads on the wheel discs if the pads are worn
- the vehicle is **travelling faster** – a faster vehicle has greater kinetic energy.

The thinking distance increases linearly:
- Double speed = Double the distance travelled whilst reacting (at constant speed).

The distance follows a squared relationship:
- Double speed = Quadruple the braking distance.
- Triple speed = Multiply the braking distance by 9.

Thinking, Braking and Stopping Distances

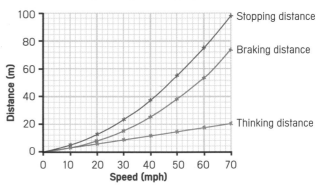

P3 Work and Power

Work

When lifting an object, the force applied will be the same as the weight of the object, measured in newtons:

> Weight (N) = Mass (kg) × Gravitational field (N/kg)

Work is done whenever a **force** moves an object. Energy is **transferred** to the object. You do work and develop power during everyday activities, for example:

- **lifting** weights
- **climbing** stairs
- **pulling** a rubbish bin
- **pushing** a shopping trolley.

Energy is needed to do work. Both energy and work are measured in **joules (J)**.

Work done is equal to the energy transferred (from one form to another).

> Work done (J) = Energy transferred (J)

The amount of work done depends on the:

- **size of the force** (in newtons)
- **distance** the object is moved (in metres).

> Work done (J) = Force applied (N) × Distance moved in direction of force (m)

Power

Power is a measure of how quickly work is done. Power is measured in **watts (W)**.

Some cars have much higher power ratings than others and may also use more fuel. High fuel consumption is:

- expensive for the driver
- damaging to the environment.

Power, work done and time taken are linked by this formula:

> $$\text{Power (W)} = \frac{\text{Work done (J)}}{\text{Time (s)}}$$

Example 1
A girl does 2400 joules of work when she runs up a flight of stairs in 8 seconds. Calculate her power.

$$\text{Power} = \frac{\text{Work done}}{\text{Time}} = \frac{2400}{8s} = \textbf{300W}$$

(HT) The **work done** and **power** formulae can be rearranged to work out distance moved or time taken.

Example 2
A crane does 200 000J of work when it lifts a load of 25 000N. The power of the crane is 50kW.

Calculate the time taken to move the load.

$$\text{Time} = \frac{\text{Work done}}{\text{Power}}$$

Power must be in watts

$$= \frac{200\ 000J}{50\ 000W}$$

$$= \textbf{4s}$$

If the speed of an object is known, power can be calculated from:

> Power (W) = Force (N) × Velocity (m/s)

Fuel Consumption

The data shows fuel consumption for two petrol cars. Car 1 has a more **powerful** engine. It travels fewer miles for each gallon of fuel – it uses more petrol per mile than Car 2, so it will be more expensive to run and more harmful to the environment.

	Engine Size (litres)	Fuel Consumption (mpg)	
		Urban	Non-urban
Car 1	1.6	29	49
Car 2	1.0	47	71

Key Words   Transfer • Energy • Joules (J) • Power

Kinetic Energy

Kinetic energy is the energy an object has because of its movement. A ball rolling along the ground, a car travelling along a road and a boy running all have kinetic energy.

The kinetic energy of an object depends on:

- its mass (kg)
- its speed (m/s).

A moving car has kinetic energy.

- If a car moves with a greater speed it has more kinetic energy.
- If a car has greater mass it has more kinetic energy.

(HT) Cars with a greater kinetic energy will have a greater braking distance.

You can calculate kinetic energy by using this formula:

$$\text{Kinetic energy (J)} = \frac{1}{2} \times \text{Mass (kg)} \times \text{Speed}^2 \text{ (m/s)}^2$$

KE
$\frac{1}{2} \times m \times v^2$

where v = speed

Example

A car of mass 1000kg is moving at a speed of 10m/s. How much kinetic energy does it have?

$$\text{Kinetic energy} = \frac{1}{2} \times \text{Mass} \times \text{Speed}^2$$
$$= \frac{1}{2} \times 1000\text{kg} \times (10\text{m/s})^2$$
$$= 50\,000\text{J (or 50kJ)}$$

Fuel for Vehicles

Most cars rely on petrol or diesel (which come from fossil fuels which are running out) for their energy. But, electricity can also be used, i.e. cars can be driven by battery power or solar power. Cars powered by fossil fuels pollute the environment at the point of use. Battery-powered cars don't do this, but recharging the batteries uses electricity which is generated in power stations. And power stations do cause pollution.

(HT) Biofuels are a possible alternative to fossil fuels. Biofuelled and solar powered vehicles reduce pollution at point of use, which may lead to an overall decrease in CO_2 emissions. But they do produce pollution during production.

Car fuel consumption depends on the:

- energy required to increase the kinetic energy
- energy required to work against friction
- driving style, speed and road conditions.

Frictional Forces

Frictional forces, such as drag, friction and air resistance, can act against the movement of the object, slowing it down. These forces can be reduced by:

- changing the shape of the object
- using a lubricant (to make the object slide through the air with less resistance).

The shape of an object can influence its top speed:

- Badminton shuttlecocks increase air resistance so they travel slowly.

- Parachutes have a larger surface area to increase air resistance.
- Roof boxes on cars and open windows increase air resistance.
- Deflectors on lorries reduce air resistance.
- Wedge-shaped sports cars reduce air resistance.

Greater drag can lead to energy loss and inefficiency (and greater fuel consumption) by vehicles.

P3 Crumple Zones

Car Safety Features for Protection

Modern cars have **safety features** that absorb energy in a collision, for example:

- **Seatbelts**, which prevent people in the car from being propelled forwards (though may cause bruising).
- **Air bags**, which cushion the impact for the driver and passengers.
- A **crumple zone**, a part of the car designed to 'crumple' during a collision.
- A **collapsible steering column**, which absorbs energy and breaks to avoid the driver being impaled during an accident.

These features **change shape** during an impact to absorb energy. They protect occupants and reduce the risk of injury during a collision. Seatbelts have to be replaced after a crash because they can be damaged by the forces they experience.

A **safety cage** is a metal cage which strengthens the cabin section of the car. It prevents the vehicle from collapsing when upside down or rolling.

Safety cages don't absorb energy – they remain rigid to prevent the car collapsing on the passengers.

Crumple zone

Car Safety Features for Prevention

Some car safety features are designed to prevent accidents. Some features make the car itself safer:

- **Anti-lock braking systems** (ABS) prevent the tyres from skidding. This stops the vehicle more quickly and allows the driver to control the steering.
- **Traction control** prevents the car from skidding while accelerating. This helps the driver to get out of a dangerous situation quickly.

Some features help the driver by removing distractions:

- **Electric windows** make it easier for drivers to open and close the windows whilst driving.
- **Paddle shift controls** allow drivers to keep both hands on the steering wheel when changing gear or adjusting the stereo.

HT Anti-lock braking systems (ABS) prevent the tyres from skidding. They work by pumping the brakes on and off automatically. This increases the area of the tyres that is in contact with the road. **Friction** between the two surfaces is increased, so the braking distance is reduced, and the car is able to stop more quickly.

Momentum

During a collision a quantity called **momentum** is conserved.

When the car slows down during impact its momentum decreases. As it decreases, the passengers feel a force which can result in injury, e.g. whiplash.

You can calculate momentum using this equation:

$$\text{Momentum} = \text{Mass} \times \text{Velocity}$$

The force experienced by a passenger during a collision depends upon the rate of changes of momentum. The quicker the change in momentum, the greater the force experienced.

Use the following equation to calculate the force:

$$\text{Force (N)} = \frac{\text{Change in momentum (kg m/s)}}{\text{Time taken (s)}}$$

Change in momentum = $m_2 v_2 - m_1 v_1$

where m_1 = initial mass, m_2 = final mass, v_1 = initial velocity, v_2 = final velocity

The quicker the body decelerates, the greater the force felt by the body.

Example 1

Calculate the force experienced when an 80kg man decelerates from 3m/s to rest (0m/s) in 0.5 seconds.

$$\text{Force} = \frac{(80 \times 0) - (80 \times 3)}{0.5}$$

Force = **480N**

Example 2

Recalculate the force experienced by the same man, if he now increases the time taken to stop to 2 seconds.

$$\text{Force} = \frac{(80 \times 0) - (80 \times 3)}{2}$$

Force = **120N**

Compare the forces experienced in the collisions in Example 1 and Example 2.

HT Reducing Stopping Forces

The stopping forces experienced in a collision can be **reduced** by:

- **increasing** the stopping or **collision time**
- **increasing** the stopping or **collision distance**.

All of the standard safety features reduce the stopping forces on the people in the car. This reduces the risk of injury.

Using **Newton's Second Law of Motion**:

Driving force (f)	=	Mass (kg)	×	Acceleration (m/s²)
F	=	m	×	a

If the collision stopping time is increased (using a crumple zone, for example), the rate of acceleration is decreased so the force is decreased.

Quick Test

1. List the main features of cars designed to prevent accidents.
2. What feature on a lorry reduces air resistance?
3. HT How does an increase in collision time affect the force felt by the driver?

P3 Falling Safely

Terminal Speed

When a skydiver jumps out of an aeroplane, the speed of his descent can be considered in two separate parts:

- **Before the parachute opens** (when the skydiver is in free-fall).
- **After the parachute opens** (when air resistance is greatly increased).

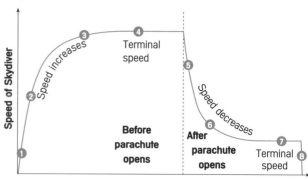

Before the Parachute Opens

1. When the skydiver jumps, he initially accelerates due to the force of **gravity**.
2. As he falls, he experiences the **frictional force of air resistance** (R) in the opposite direction. At this point, **weight** (W) is **greater than R**, so he continues to accelerate.
3. As his speed increases, so does the air resistance acting on him.
4. Air resistance increases until it's equal to W. The resultant force now acting on him is zero and his falling speed becomes **constant** as forces are balanced. This speed is called the terminal speed.

After the Parachute Opens

5. When the parachute is opened, unbalanced forces act again because the upward force of R is greatly increased and is bigger than W.
6. The increase in R decreases his speed. As his speed decreases, so does R.
7. R decreases until it's equal to W. The forces acting are once again balanced and, for the second time, he falls at a steady speed, although slower than before. This is a **new terminal speed**.

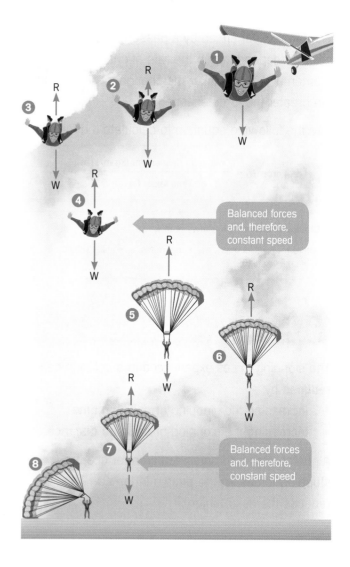

Balanced forces and, therefore, constant speed

Balanced forces and, therefore, constant speed

(HT) At **higher speeds**, falling objects experience **more drag**. If you **increase the area** of the object that's facing downwards, **you increase the drag**.

The **terminal speed** occurs when the drag is equal to the weight of the object.

Air resistance • Terminal speed

HT Terminal Speed

When an object falls at its **terminal speed**:
- the speed isn't changing so the kinetic energy doesn't increase.

- the GPE decreases as the object does work against friction (GPE is transferred into internal or thermal energy of the surrounding air particles by friction).

Weight and Mass

Weight is due to the force of gravity on an object. The **mass** of an object is the amount of matter that it contains. Weight and mass are linked by two related formulae:

| Weight (N) | = | Mass (kg) | × | Gravitational field strength (N/kg) |

| Weight (N) | = | Mass (kg) | × | Acceleration of free-fall (m/s²) |

$$\frac{W}{m \times g}$$

where g = gravitational field strength or acceleration of free-fall

Without air resistance, a falling object near the Earth's surface would have an acceleration of 10m/s^2. This is known as the **acceleration of free-fall, g**.

The force which causes this acceleration is the weight of the object. The formula is W = mg.

Example 1
Calculate the weight of a falling stone of mass 0.1kg, if $g = 10 \text{m/s}^2$.

Weight = Mass × Acceleration of free-fall
= $0.1 \text{kg} \times 10 \text{m/s}^2$ = **1N**

Near the surface of the Earth the **gravitational field strength**, g, is 10N/kg which means that every 1kg of matter experiences a downwards force, or has a weight, of 10N.

Example 2
Calculate the weight of a stone of mass 0.1kg on Earth, if g is 10N/kg.

Weight = Mass × Gravitational field strength
= $0.1 \text{kg} \times 10 \text{N/kg}$ = **1N**

N.B. Acceleration of free-fall and gravitational field strength are numerically the same, i.e. 10m/s^2 and 10N/kg. They also both have the same symbol, g.

Gravity

Gravitational field strength or acceleration due to gravity:
- is unaffected by atmospheric changes
- varies slightly at different points on the Earth's surface

- will be slightly different on the top of a mountain or down a mineshaft.

Quick Test

1. Which two forces on a skydiver are equal when he/she is falling at terminal speed?
2. HT When an object falls at its terminal speed, what happens to its kinetic energy?

P3 The Energy of Games and Theme Rides

Gravitational Potential Energy

The **gravitational potential energy (GPE)** of an object is the energy stored due to:

- its position in the Earth's gravitational field (height)
- its **mass**.

Any object with the **potential** to fall has gravitational potential energy, for example, a person standing on a diving board (before they jump off).

Man A standing on a higher diving board will have **more GPE** than man B standing on a lower diving board (providing they have the same mass). This is because the higher man is further away from the ground.

A heavier man, man C, standing on the **same diving board** as man A will have **more GPE**. This is because the heavier man has a **bigger mass**.

You can calculate GPE using this formula:

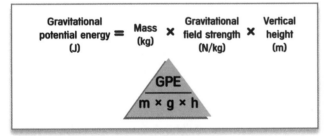

Gravitational field strength, g, is a constant. On Earth it has a value of 10N/kg. This means that every 1kg of matter near the surface of the Earth experiences a downward force of 10N due to gravity.

On planets where the gravitational field strength is higher, the gravitational potential energy is greater.

(HT) Examples of GPE

Example 1

A skier of mass 80kg gets on a ski lift which takes her from a height of 1000m to a height of 3000m. By how much does her gravitational potential energy increase?

= 80kg × 10N/kg × (3000m − 1000m)

= 80kg × 10N/kg × 2000m

= 1 600 000J (or 1600kJ)

N.B. Work done by the ski lift motor has been transferred into gravitational potential energy for the skier.

Example 2

A ball is kicked vertically upwards from the ground. Its mass is 0.2kg and it increases its gravitational potential energy by 30J when it reaches the top point in its flight. What height does the ball reach?

Rearrange the formula:

$$\text{Vertical height} = \frac{\text{GPE}}{\text{Mass} \times \text{Gravitational field strength}}$$

$$= \frac{30J}{0.2kg \times 10N/kg} = \textbf{15m}$$

Gravitational potential energy (GPE) • Mass

GPE and Kinetic Energy

When an object falls, it converts **gravitational potential energy (GPE)** into **kinetic energy (KE)**. For example, this happens when:

- a diver jumps off a diving board
- a ball rolls down a hill
- a skydiver jumps out of a plane.

Many theme park rides, for example rollercoasters, also use this transfer of energy.

If the **mass** of a rollercoaster car is **doubled**, the kinetic energy also **doubles**.

If the **speed** of the car is **doubled**, the kinetic energy **quadruples**.

Increasing the **gravitational field strength**, **g**, will increase the gravitational potential energy. However this couldn't ever happen on Earth as gravitational field strength is **constant**.

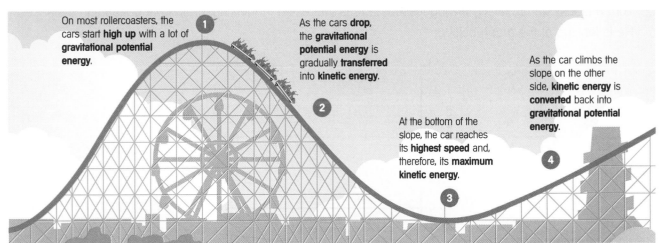

On most rollercoasters, the cars start **high up** with a lot of **gravitational potential energy**. **1**

As the cars **drop**, the **gravitational potential energy** is gradually **transferred** into **kinetic energy**. **2**

At the bottom of the slope, the car reaches its **highest speed** and, therefore, its **maximum kinetic energy**. **3**

As the car climbs the slope on the other side, **kinetic energy** is **converted** back into **gravitational potential energy**. **4**

(HT) As an object falls the GPE is converted into kinetic energy. Remember:

$$\textbf{GPE} = \textbf{mgh} \text{ and } \textbf{KE} = \frac{1}{2}\textbf{mv}^2$$

If all of the GPE is turned into KE:

$$mgh = \frac{1}{2}mv^2$$

The m on each side cancels, leaving:

$$gh = \frac{1}{2}v^2 \text{ or } gh = \frac{v^2}{2}$$

This can be rearranged to calculate the height, h:

$$h = \frac{v^2}{2g}$$

Example

A pot of paint falls from the top of some step ladders. Just before it hits the ground it has a velocity of 8m/s. From what height did it fall? (Remember g = 10 m/s^2)

$$h = \frac{(8)^2}{2 \times 10}$$

$$= \frac{64}{20}$$

$$= \textbf{3.2 m}$$

Quick Test

1. What happens to the size of the kinetic energy of an object if its speed is doubled?
2. (HT) What is the value of the gravitational field strength on Earth?
3. (HT) What is the unit of GPE?

1 a) What two things do you need to know in order to calculate the acceleration of an object? **[2]**

....

b) Draw lines between the boxes to match each statement with its meaning on a speed–time graph.

Straight line with a positive gradient

Straight line with a negative gradient

Horizontal straight line

Constant speed

Deceleration

Acceleration

[2]

2 Tom has just started taking driving lessons and is interested in thinking, braking and stopping distances. He is looking at the graph below.

a) Which of the graph lines, A, B or C represents the thinking distance? **[1]**

....

b) How long would the braking distance be if a vehicle was travelling at 45mph? **[1]**

....

c) Write about the factors which increase thinking distance of a driver. **[4]**

....

....

....

3 Kinetic energy is the energy an object has because of its movement.

a) What two things does the kinetic energy of an object depend on? **[1]**

....

b) A 2000kg van is travelling at 20m/s. Calculate its kinetic energy. **[2]**

....

4 Describe three safety features of modern cars that protect the occupants in the event of a collision. **[3]**

....

....

5 Put the following sentences into the correct order by numbering them **1** to **4**. **[3]**

A The skydiver reaches a very high terminal speed where air resistance is equal to his weight. ⬚

B The skydiver slows down to reach a lower terminal speed. ⬚

C As the skydiver falls, his speed increases because his weight is greater than air resistance. ⬚

D When he opens his parachute, the air resistance becomes greater than his weight. ⬚

6 Calculate the height of a 160g cricket ball if it has 30J of gravitational potential energy. **[2]**

....

....

7 a) William has a car of mass 1100kg. He slows down from 50 mph (22.3m/s) to 30 mph **[2]**
(13.4m/s) as he drives into a village. Calculate the change in momentum of the car.

....

(HT)

b) As William drives, a girl runs into the road and he has to do an emergency stop. He reduces his speed from 13.4m/s to rest in 2.2s.

i) Calculate the change in momentum of the car. **[2]**

....

ii) What force must the brakes apply to stop the car in this time? **[2]**

....

8 A new theme park ride lifts its occupants vertically. It then drops vertically downwards under the influence of gravity. **[3]**
Assuming there is no energy loss (as heat or sound), calculate the maximum velocity reached after the ride has dropped 30m. (Use $g = 10m/s^2$)

....

P4 Sparks

Generating Static Electricity

An insulating material can become electrically **charged** if it's rubbed with another insulating material. **Electrons** (which have a negative charge) transfer from one material to the other, leaving:

- one material with a **positive** charge
- one material with a **negative** charge.

You can generate **static electricity** by rubbing a balloon, comb or strip of plastic against a jumper. The electrically charged object will attract very small objects, e.g. pieces of paper or cork.

Dusting brushes can be charged so that they attract dust when they pass over the brush.

Synthetic clothing can become charged due to **friction** between the clothing and the person's body when the clothes are put on. When the clothing is removed from the body, static sparks are sometimes produced.

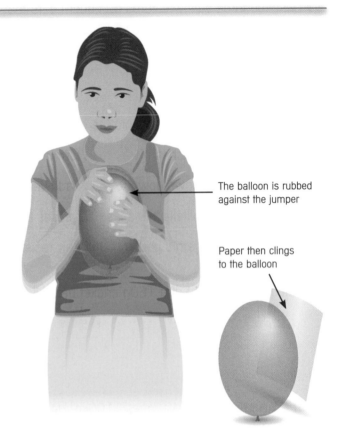

The balloon is rubbed against the jumper

Paper then clings to the balloon

Discharging Static Electricity

A **charged object** can be **discharged** (i.e. have the excess charge removed) by **earthing** it. When an object discharges, electrons are transferred from the charged object to earth.

If you become charged and then earthed, you could get an **electrostatic shock**.

For example, you can become charged by friction between the soles of your feet and the floor if you're walking on an insulator such as carpet or vinyl. If you then touch a **water pipe**, e.g. a radiator, the charge is earthed and discharge occurs, giving you a shock.

Problems of Static Electricity

In some situations, static electricity can be a **nuisance**.

For example, static can cause:

- dirt and dust to be attracted to insulating materials, e.g. television screens and computer monitors
- some materials to cling to your skin.

In other situations, static electricity can be very **dangerous**:

- Flour mills and petrochemical factories have atmospheres that can contain extremely flammable gases (or vapours), or high concentrations of oxygen. A discharge of static electricity (i.e. a spark) can lead to an explosion.
- Static is dangerous in any situation where large amounts could flow through your body to earth, for example, lightning.

Key Words   **Electron • Static electricity • Friction • Earthed**

Repulsion and Attraction

Two insulating materials with the **same charge** will repel each other. For example, if a **positively charged** Perspex rod is held near to a suspended **positively charged** Perspex rod, the suspended rod will be **repelled**. The same thing would happen if both rods had a negative charge.

Two insulating materials with **different charges** will attract each other. For example, if a **negatively charged** ebonite rod is held near to a suspended **positively charged** Perspex rod, the suspended rod will be **attracted** to the ebonite rod. This would also happen if the charges were the other way round.

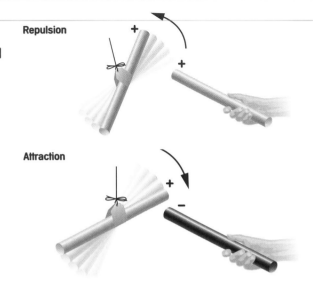

Repulsion

Attraction

HT Charging Up Objects

Electric or static charge builds up when **electrons** (negatively charged) are rubbed off one material onto another.

- The material that **receives** the electrons becomes **negatively charged** due to an **excess of electrons**.
- The material **giving up the** electrons becomes **positively charged** due to a **loss of electrons**.

A Perspex rod rubbed with a cloth gives up electrons and becomes positively charged. The cloth receives the electrons and becomes negatively charged.

An ebonite rod rubbed with fur receives electrons and becomes negatively charged. The fur gives up electrons and becomes positively charged.

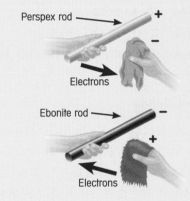

Perspex rod

Electrons

Ebonite rod

Electrons

Atoms and molecules that have become charged are called **ions**.

- If they have an excess of electrons they are **negative ions**.
- If they have lost electrons they are **positive ions**.

Reducing the Danger

The chance of receiving an electric shock can be **reduced** by:

- making sure appliances are correctly earthed
- using insulation mats effectively
- wearing shoes with insulating soles.

Lorries that contain inflammable gases, liquids or powders need to be earthed before unloading, as friction can cause a build-up of charge. This charge could lead to a spark, which could then ignite the flammable substance.

Anti-static sprays, liquids and cloths help to reduce the problems of static electricity by preventing the transfer of charge from one insulator to another. If there is no build-up of charge, there can't be any discharge.

P4 Uses of Electrostatics

Using Static in Everyday Life

Static electricity is used in many ways, including spray painting, smoke precipitators and defibrillators.

Spray Painting

The paint particles are given a negative charge so that they repel each other, forming a fine spray. This ensures that the paint is applied evenly. The panel to be sprayed is positively charged so it attracts the negatively charged paint. This means that less paint is wasted and even the back and sides of the object, in the shadow of the spray, receive a coat of paint.

In a similar way, electrostatics can be used in crop-spraying.

(HT) The paint gains electrons as it passes through the nozzle of the gun, so becomes negatively charged. The car panel has lost electrons so is left positively charged. The car attracts the oppositely charged paint. As the paint sticks to the car, the charges cancel so the car becomes neutrally charged and no more paint is attracted. The car receives an even coat of paint.

Spray Painting

Negatively charged nozzle

Negatively charged particles of paint

Car panel positively charged

Smoke Precipitators

Electrostatic dust precipitators can remove smoke particles from chimneys. Metal grids are installed in the chimney and are connected to a high potential difference (voltage). The dust becomes positively charged as it passes the grid, inducing a positive charge on the dust. The dust particles are attracted to the negative charged plates, where they form large particles that fall back down the chimney when they are heavy enough, or if the plates are stuck.

(HT) The dust particles become charged when they lose electrons.

Smoke Precipitator

Waste gases

Smoke and waste gases

Defibrillators

Electricity can be used to start the heart when it has stopped. Two paddles are charged and are put in good electrical contact with the patient's chest using gel. Taking care not to shock the operator, charge is then passed through the patient to make the heart contract.

Defibrillator

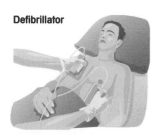

Circuits

A **circuit** is a complete loop that allows an **electrical current** to flow. **Electrons** flow around the circuit from the **negative electrode** of the power source to the **positive electrode**. But this was only discovered recently so circuit diagrams are drawn showing the current flowing from **the positive to the negative** electrode.

Fixed and Variable Resistors

Resistance is a measure of how hard it is to get a current through a **component** in a circuit at a particular **voltage** (potential difference). Resistance is measured in **ohms** (Ω).

The current through a circuit can be controlled by varying the resistance. There are two types of resistor:

- **A fixed resistor** has **constant** resistance. The bigger the resistance, the smaller the current that flows for a particular voltage.
- **A variable resistor** (or rheostat) has a **changeable** resistance.

The resistance of the rheostat can be changed by moving the slider, changing the length of wire between the contacts.

- Long wire = high resistance, low current.
- Short wire = low resistance, large current.

Variable Resistors

High resistance
Sliding the contrast

Low resistance

Current, Voltage and Resistance

For a **given resistor, current increases** as **voltage increases** (and vice versa). For a **fixed voltage, current decreases** as **resistance increases** (and vice versa).

Current, voltage and resistance are related by this formula:

Resistance (Ω) = $\dfrac{\text{Voltage (V)}}{\text{Current (A)}}$

$$\frac{V}{R \times I}$$

where I is the current

Example 1

Calculate the resistance of the lamp in the circuit:

$$\text{Resistance} = \frac{\text{Voltage}}{\text{Current}} = \frac{3V}{0.2A} = 15\Omega$$

HT Example 2

Calculate the reading on the ammeter in this circuit if the bulb has a resistance of 20 ohms.

$$\text{Current} = \frac{\text{Voltage}}{\text{Resistance}} = \frac{6V}{20\Omega} = 0.3A$$

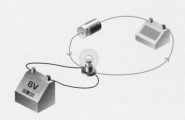

P4 Safe Electricals

Live, Neutral and Earth Wires

Electrical appliances are connected to mains electricity by a cable and 3-pin plug. Most cables and plugs contain three wires:

- **Live wire** (brown) – carries current to the appliance at a high voltage (230V).
- **Neutral wire** (blue) – completes the circuit and carries current away from the appliance.
- **Earth wire** (green and yellow) – safety wire that stops the appliance becoming live.

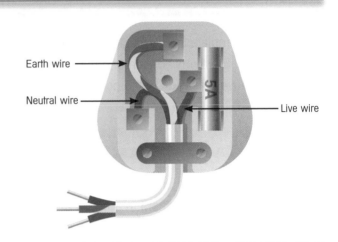

Earth wire

Neutral wire

5A

Live wire

Double Insulation

All appliances with outer metal cases (**conductors**) have an **earth wire**, so they are **earthed**. An earthed conductor can't become live.

Appliances with **cases made of** insulators don't have an earth wire (although they still have a **fuse**). They are **double insulated** so they can't become live.

HT Earthing

Electrical appliances with outer metal cases are earthed in order to protect the appliance and the user. The earth wire and fuse work together.

1. A fault in the appliance causes the casing to become live.
2. The circuit **short-circuits** (i.e. the path of the flow of charge changes) because the earth wire offers less resistance.
3. The fuse wire melts.
4. The circuit is broken.
5. The appliance and the user are protected.

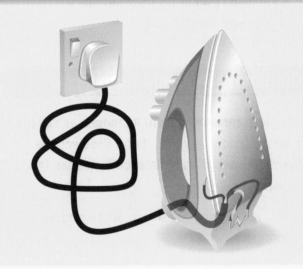

Fuses and Circuit Breakers

Fuses and circuit breakers are **safety devices** designed to break a circuit if a fault occurs. This can prevent fires, injuries and deaths.

A **fuse** is a short, thin piece of wire with a low melting point. It's used to prevent cables or appliances from overheating. To work properly, the current rating of the fuse must be **just above** the normal current that flows through the appliance.

1. A fault causes the current in the appliance to exceed the current rating of the fuse.
2. The fuse wire gets hot and melts or breaks.
3. The circuit is broken so the current is unable to flow.
4. The appliance and user are protected.

A **circuit breaker** acts in a similar way to a fuse, but it can be easily **reset** rather than replaced.

Key Words   Conductor • Insulator • Fuse • Circuit breaker

Power

The power rating of a device tells you how quickly electrical energy is being changed (transferred) into another form within that device. Power is measured in Watts (W). For example, a 2400W hairdryer changes electrical energy into heat and **kinetic energy** (as well as some sound) at a rate of 2400 joules each second.

Power (W)	=	Current (A)	×	Voltage (V)

(HT) Calculate the current which flows in a 2400W hairdryer, when it is plugged in to the 230V mains supply.

$$I = \frac{P}{V}$$

$$= \frac{2400W}{230V}$$

$$= \textbf{10.4 Amps}$$

The plug should be fitted with a 13A fuse.

(HT) Example of a Fuse in Action

1. If the current flowing through an appliance is **below** the **current rating** of the fuse, the appliance will work properly.
2. But, if a fault occurs inside the appliance, the live wire will make contact with the neutral wire. The current flowing would then be **higher** than the **current rating** of the fuse due to lower resistance.
3. This causes the fuse wire to get hotter and hotter until it melts and breaks the circuit. The current is unable to flow so there is no danger of the flex overheating (resulting in a fire). Further damage to the appliance, or injury to the user, is prevented.

Fuses and circuit breakers prevent:
- injury and death as they stop appliances from becoming 'live'
- fires as they stop cables and flexes from overheating
- damage to the components of an appliance because they break the circuit if a higher than normal current flows through the appliance.

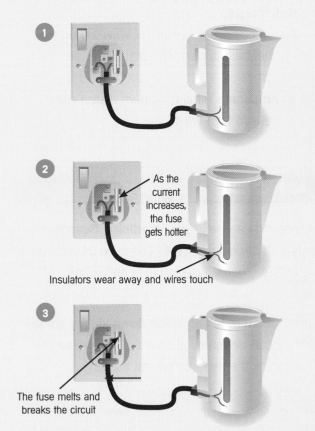

As the current increases, the fuse gets hotter

Insulators wear away and wires touch

The fuse melts and breaks the circuit

Quick Test

1. State the equation used to calculate resistance.
2. Name the wires in a three-pin plug and give the colour of each.
3. What happens to a fuse when too much current flows through it?
4. (HT) Fuses and circuit breakers are used to prevent what three things?

Key Words	Kinetic energy	61

P4 Ultrasound

Ultrasound

Ultrasound is sound waves with frequencies above the upper limit of the human hearing range (i.e. above about 20 000 hertz (Hz)).

Ultrasound travels in a **longitudinal wave**. This can be demonstrated using a slinky spring.

Key Features of Waves

The key features of waves are:

- **Rarefaction** – area of low pressure.
- **Compression** – area of high pressure.
- **Wavelength** – the distance between corresponding points on two successive disturbances.
- **Frequency** – the number of waves produced (or that pass a particular point) in 1 second.

(HT) • **Amplitude** – the maximum disturbance caused by a wave.

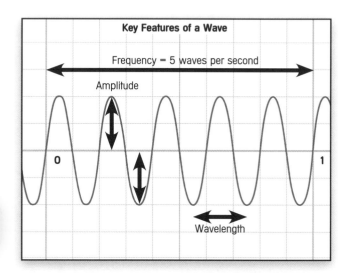

Longitudinal Wave

Direction of wave movement

Hand moves in and out

Rarefaction (coils further apart)

Compression (coils closer together)

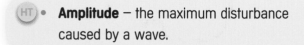

Key Features of a Wave

Frequency = 5 waves per second

Amplitude

0

1

Wavelength

Applications of Ultrasound

Ultrasound can be used in **medicine**. **Scanning** the body with ultrasound waves can build up a picture of the body's organs, including the heart, lungs and liver.

Ultrasound waves can **break down kidney stones** so they can be removed from the body naturally. This avoids the need for painful surgery.

(HT) Ultrasonic waves cause the kidney stones to vibrate. The stones break up, are dispersed, and can then be passed out of the body in urine.

Ultrasound can be used:

- to measure the **speed of blood flow**
- to detect **gallstones** and **tumours**
- for **pre-natal scanning** because there is less risk to mother or baby than using X-rays.

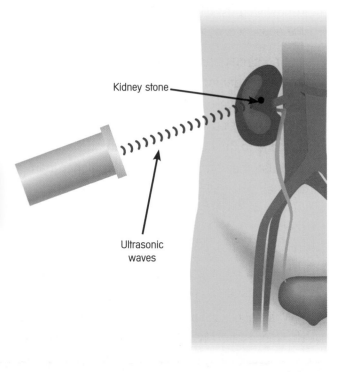

Breaking Down a Kidney Stone

Kidney stone

Ultrasonic waves

HT More on Ultrasound

Ultrasound waves are **partially reflected** at a **boundary** as they pass from one medium or substance into another. The **time taken** for these **reflections** to be **detected** can be used to calculate the depth of the reflecting surface. The reflected waves are usually processed to produce a visual image on a screen.

Ultrasound has two main advantages over X-ray imaging:

- It's able to produce images of soft tissue.
- It doesn't damage living cells.

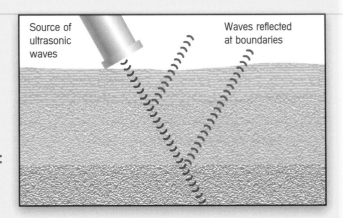

Particle Motion in Waves

All waves **transfer energy** from one point to another **without** transferring any **particles of matter**. In the following diagrams, each coil of the slinky spring represents one particle. There are two types of wave – **longitudinal** and **transverse**.

Longitudinal Waves	Transverse Waves
Each particle moves backwards and forwards about its normal position in the same plane as the direction of wave movement.	Each particle moves up and down about its normal position at 90° to the direction of the wave movement.
Direction of energy transfer Hand moves in and out	Direction of energy transfer Hand moves up and down

Quick Test

1. Write a definition for frequency.
2. State two medical uses of ultrasound.
3. What are the advantages of using ultrasound instead of X-rays?

P4 What is Radioactivity?

Radioactivity

Radioactive **materials** give out nuclear radiation from the nucleus of each of their atoms. The atoms are **unstable** and **decay naturally**.

During this decay, radiation can be given out in the form of alpha, beta and gamma rays:

- An **alpha particle** is a **helium** nucleus.
- A **beta particle** is a fast-moving **electron**.
- Gamma is an electromagnetic wave (energy).

Radiation is measured by the **number of nuclear decays emitted per second**. This number decreases with time.

Ionisation occurs when an uncharged (neutral) atom gains or loses electrons.

HT Alpha radiation is highly ionising because it's missing two electrons (it has a 2+ electric charge). It attracts electrons away from atoms it passes, leaving them positively charged.

HT Alpha Emission

During alpha emission, the atom decays by ejecting an **alpha particle** (a helium nucleus made up of two protons and two neutrons) from the nucleus.

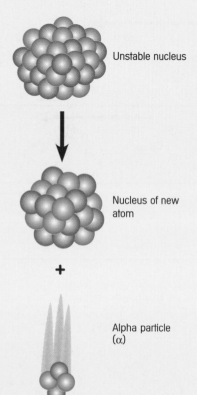

Unstable nucleus

Nucleus of new atom

+

Alpha particle (α)

The nucleus of the new atom formed differs from the original one in a number of ways:

- It is a different element.
- It has two fewer protons and two fewer neutrons.
- The atomic number has decreased by two.
- The mass number has decreased by four.

Example – alpha decay of radium-226 into radon-222:

$$^{226}_{88}\text{Ra} \longrightarrow {}^{222}_{86}\text{Rn} + {}^{4}_{2}\alpha$$

N.B. The mass numbers (at the top) and the atomic numbers (at the bottom) balance on both sides.

Beta Emission

During beta emission, the atom decays by changing a neutron into a **proton** and an **electron**. The high-energy electron ejected from the nucleus is a **beta particle**.

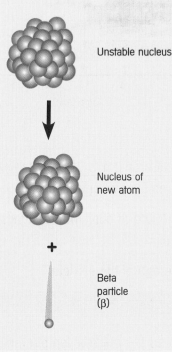

Unstable nucleus

Nucleus of new atom

+

Beta particle (β)

The nucleus of the new atom formed differs from the original one in a number of ways:

- It has one more proton and one less neutron.
- The atomic number has increased by one.
- The mass number remains the same.

Example – Beta decay of iodine-131 into xenon-131:

$$^{131}_{53}\text{I} \longrightarrow \,^{131}_{54}\text{Xe} + \,^{0}_{-1}\beta$$

N.B. The mass numbers (at the top) and the atomic numbers (at the bottom) balance on both sides.

Half-life

Half-life is the time it takes for half the undecayed nuclei in a radioactive substance to decay.

If the substance has a very **long half-life** then it remains **active** for a very **long time**.

Igneous rocks can contain uranium atoms which decay to produce stable atoms of lead. It's possible to date rocks by:

- measuring the proportion of uranium and lead in the rock
- knowing the half-life of uranium.

Atoms in a Sample of Radioactive Substance

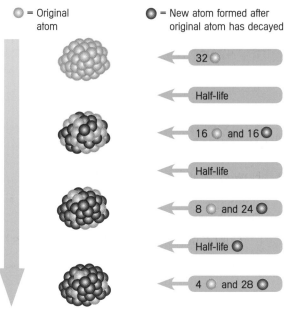

○ = Original atom   ● = New atom formed after original atom has decayed

32 ○

Half-life

16 ○ and 16 ●

Half-life

8 ○ and 24 ●

Half-life ○

4 ○ and 28 ●

N.B. This is a collection of atoms, not a nucleus.

Calculations Involving Half-life

Half-life can be calculated using a table or a graph.

Example 1

The table shows the activity of a radioactive substance against time.

Time (min)	Activity (Bq)
0	200
5	160
10	124
15	100
20	80
25	62
30	50

Calculate the half-life of the substance by:

a) using a table

b) drawing a graph.

a) Find an average by choosing three pairs of points between which the activity has halved.

Activity	Time	Half-Life
200 → 100	0 → 15	15 min
160 → 80	5 → 20	15 min
100 → 50	15 → 30	15 min

The half-life is **15 minutes**.

b)

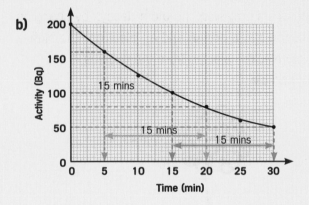

Example 2

The half-life of uranium is 700 000 000 years. Uranium forms lead when it decays.

A sample is found to contain three times as much lead as uranium.

Calculate the age of the sample.

Fraction of lead present is $\frac{3}{4}$. Fraction of uranium present is $\frac{1}{4}$.

Fraction of lead $\left(\frac{3}{4}\right)$ + Fraction of uranium $\left(\frac{1}{4}\right)$ = Original amount of uranium (1).

Work out the number of decays it takes to get $\frac{1}{4}$.

1 — half-life → $\frac{1}{2}$ — half-life → $\frac{1}{4}$ ← 2 half-lives

Age of rock = 2 × half-life

= 2 × 700 000 000 years

= **1 400 000 000 years**

Quick Test

1. How is radiation measured?
2. A substance with a very long half-life remains active for a very short time. True or false?
3. Describe an alpha particle.
4. **HT** During beta emission, the atom decays by changing a neutron into what?

Background Radiation

Background **radiation** occurs naturally in our environment and is all around us. **Most** background radiation is released by:

- radioactive substances in soil and rocks
- **cosmic rays** from outer space.

Some background radiation comes from man-made sources and waste products. Industry and hospitals both contribute to background radiation levels, but this is only a small percentage of the total background radiation.

Tracers

Radioisotopes are used as tracers in industry and hospitals. In industry, tracers are used to:

- track the dispersal of waste
- find leaks and blockages in underground pipes
- find the routes of underground pipes.

A radioactive material that emits gamma rays is put into the pipe. (Gamma is used because

it can penetrate through the soil to the surface.) The progress of the material is then tracked by a detector above ground. If there is a:

- **leak** – the radioactive material will **escape** and be detected at the surface
- **blockage** – the radioactive material will **stop flowing** so it can't be detected after this point.

Smoke Detectors

Most smoke detectors contain **Americium-241**, an **alpha emitter**. Emitted particles cause air particles to **ionise**, and the ions formed are attracted to the oppositely charged electrodes. This results in a flow of electric current. This is what happens when smoke enters the space between the two electrodes:

1 The alpha particles are absorbed by the smoke particles.

2 Less **ionisation** takes place.

3 A smaller current than normal now flows, and the alarm sounds.

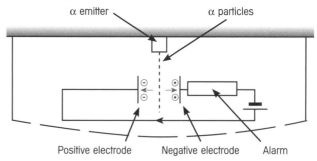

α emitter   α particles

Positive electrode   Negative electrode   Alarm

Carbon Dating

A small amount of the carbon in our atmosphere and the bodies of animals and plants is radioactive Carbon-14.

Measurements from **radioactive carbon** can be used to **date** old, once-living materials, such as wood.

(HT) The activity of radioactive carbon can be used to find the approximate age of a once-living material. The amount of radioactive Carbon-14 in the atmosphere has remained unchanged for thousands of years. A dead object doesn't exchange gases with the air as living matter does. As the Carbon-14

in the dead object **decays**, it is not replaced so the radioactivity of the sample **decreases**.

So, the dead object will have a different radioactivity to living matter. The **ratio** of these two activities can be used to find a fairly accurate approximate age for the object within known limits (approximately 50 years).

P4 Treatment

Radiation

X-rays and gamma rays are **electromagnetic waves** with similar **wavelengths** but they are produced in different ways.

X-rays and nuclear **radiation** (i.e. gamma and beta radiation) can be used in medicine.

X-rays can be used to build up a picture of the inside of a patient's body. The person in a hospital who takes X-rays and uses radiation is called a **radiographer**.

Medical radioisotopes are produced by placing materials in a nuclear reactor. They become radioactive when they absorb extra neutrons.

Gamma rays **damage cells**, so they can be used to **treat cancer**.

Gamma (and sometimes beta) can pass through the skin (unlike alpha), so can be used as medical **tracers** (i.e. to track the progress of a substance through a patient's system). They are only inside the body for a short time to avoid damage to healthy tissue.

Gamma rays can also be used to **sterilise medical equipment** because they kill germs and bacteria.

(HT) X-rays are made by firing high-speed **electrons** at metal targets. X-rays are easier to control than gamma rays.

After alpha or beta decay, a nucleus sometimes contains surplus energy. It emits this as gamma radiation, which is very high frequency electromagnetic radiation.

Treating Cancer

Gamma rays can be used to treat cancer:

1. A wide beam of **gamma rays** from a source outside the body is focused on the tumour.
2. The beam is rotated around the outside of the body with the tumour at the centre.
3. This concentrates the gamma rays on the tumour, but minimises damage to the rest of the body.

Gamma radiation treatment can destroy cancer cells without the need for surgery, but it may damage healthy cells and cause sickness.

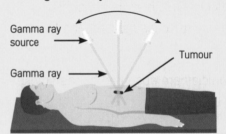

Gamma ray source

Gamma ray

Tumour

Tracers

Tracers are small amounts of radioactive materials (with a short half-life) which are swallowed or injected into a patient. The tracer spreads through the body, whilst its progress is followed using an external radiation detector (a gamma camera).

For example, the thyroid gland in the neck affects the body's metabolic rate. It absorbs iodine, so a patient can be given a tracer which contains radioactive iodine-131. A detector follows the progress of a tracer. You can tell how well the gland is working by measuring the amount of iodine it absorbs.

*N.B. The radioactive material **must** emit either gamma or beta radiation, because they both pass through skin so they can be detected outside the body.*

Producing Electricity

Power stations use **energy sources** to produce electricity.

Conventional power stations **burn** **fossil fuels** (coal, oil and gas). This produces heat which boils water and creates **steam**.

Nuclear power stations use **uranium**. A nuclear reaction takes place which produces the heat required to make **steam**. The nuclear reaction is called **fission**.

Both power stations then **use the steam** to drive turbines, which turn generators and produce electricity.

Nuclear Reactor

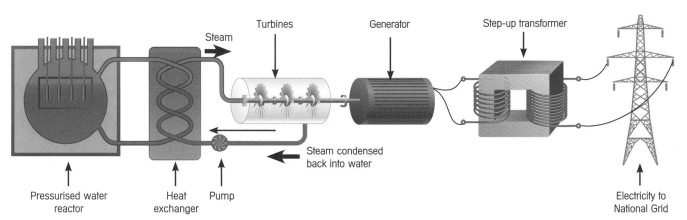

Steam

Turbines

Generator

Step-up transformer

Pressurised water reactor

Heat exchanger

Pump

Steam condensed back into water

Electricity to National Grid

Fission

Nuclear fission is the process by which heat energy is released when a radioactive nucleus (i.e. uranium) **splits**. This heat energy can be used in a nuclear reactor.

When a uranium nucleus absorbs an extra neutron it splits, releasing energy and more neutrons. These neutrons can then cause further uranium nuclei to split. This is called a **chain reaction**.

Nuclear fission produces radioactive waste, which can be dangerous.

A nuclear bomb is a chain reaction that has gone out of control. It results in one powerful release of energy.

P4 Fission and Fusion

Fusion

Nuclear fusion is the process by which heat energy is released when nuclei join (**fuse**) together. Fusion happens easily in stars, but is not yet a practical energy resource on Earth.

HT Small Scale Nuclear Fission

1. The uranium atom is hit with a neutron.
2. The nucleus splits into two smaller nuclei (e.g. barium and krypton).
3. Energy and new neutrons are released.
4. The new atoms formed (barium and krypton), are themselves radioactive.

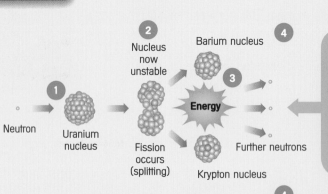

Neutron — Uranium nucleus

① Nucleus now unstable

② Fission occurs (splitting)

Barium nucleus

Energy

③ Further neutrons

Krypton nucleus

④

If more than one neutron is released when the uranium nucleus splits, these neutrons can cause further uranium nuclei to split. This is called a **chain reaction**.

Large Scale Nuclear Fission

Scientists stop nuclear reactions getting out of control by placing **control rods** in the reactor.

The rods absorb some of the neutrons (preventing further fissions).

They can be lowered or raised to control the number of neutrons available for fission, which allows the process to keep operating safely.

Energy

The energy is released in the form of heat. Each fission reaction only produces a tiny amount of energy, but there are billions and billions of reactions every second.

The new neutrons produced can each cause further uranium nuclei to split, so more fission reactions are created. This is a **chain reaction**, so it carries on and on and on.

Nuclear Fusion

When two nuclei **join** (fuse) together a large amount of **heat energy is released**. This can only happen at **extremely** high temperatures.

It is very difficult to manage these high temperatures, so **nuclear fusion** is **not** yet a possible energy source on Earth.

An example of a fusion reaction is when two hydrogen nuclei join to form a helium nucleus. This takes place in stars and fusion bombs (also called H-bombs or hydrogen bombs).

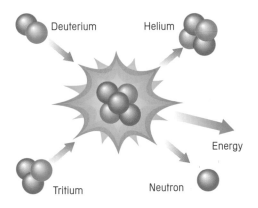

(HT) Different isotopes of hydrogen can undergo fusion:

| Deuterium | + | Tritium | → | Helium-3 |
| ^1_1H | + | ^2_1H | → | ^3_2H |

In **stars**, fusion happens very easily. On Earth, scientists have **not yet** been able to produce the **extremely high temperatures and pressures** needed to keep a fusion reaction going long enough for practical power generation.

In a fusion bomb the initial high temperatures needed are produced by a fission reaction.

Quick Test

1. What are the three types of nuclear radiation?
2. Which type of radiation is used to treat cancer?
3. Which type of radiation releases high energy electrons?

Cold Fusion

Ordinarily, fusion reactions require extremely high temperatures and pressures for two nuclei to fuse (join) together. When two nuclei fuse, energy is released. For decades, scientists have been attempting to reproduce fusion reactions under controlled conditions in laboratories. If the reaction can be controlled then the energy released could be harnessed and used as an alternative energy source, replacing fossil fuels. **Cold fusion** refers to a fusion reaction that occurs at room temperature.

In 1989 **Martin Fleischmann** and **Stanley Pons** claimed to have achieved a cold fusion reaction. When a new discovery is made, it's important to **share data** with other scientists. Scientists from across the world are then able to try to **replicate** the experiment. They must check that the experiment can be repeated and that the same

data can be produced. This shows that the discovery is genuine (i.e. it hasn't been invented, e.g. for publicity) and it doesn't show **anomalous results** (errors). It's only when experiments are repeated, and matching data collected (over and over again) that a new theory can be accepted. The data produced by Fleischmann and Pons couldn't be replicated.

(HT) Despite over 20 years of research since Fleischmann and Pons' claims, nobody has been able to successfully reproduce their experiment. Until data from cold fusion experiments can be gathered in repeated experiments and the reaction sustained to produce large quantities of energy, cold fusion isn't a realistic method of energy production.

P4 Exam Practice Questions

1 a) *The build up of charge is due to the transfer of positive electrons.* Is this statement **true** or **false**? **[1]**
Explain your answer.

....

....

b) Suggest two uses of electrostatics. **[2]**

....

2 a) Draw lines between the boxes to link each type of wire to its correct colour. **[2]**

Neutral		Green and yellow
Earth		Brown
Live		Blue

b) *Double insulated appliances require neither a fuse nor an earth wire.* Is this statement **true** or **false**? **[1]**
Explain your answer. ....

3 a) A 12V supply causes a current of 0.3A to flow through a bulb. Calculate the resistance. **[2]**

....

b) The bulb is replaced by one with a resistance of 80Ω. What is the new current in the circuit? **[2]**

....

4 Describe nuclear fusion and explain why it is not yet a possible energy resource on Earth. **[6]**

   ✎ *The quality of your written communication will be assessed in your answer to this question.*

....

....

....

....

....

....

....

HT

5 The explosion at the Chernobyl Nuclear Reactor released a large cloud of radioactive gas into the atmosphere, which spread over Europe. The gas contained caesium-137 (with a half-life of 30 years) and iodine-131. The following table shows measurements of the count rate from a small sample of iodine-131.

Time (Days)	0	4	8	12
Count Rate (Bq)	320	230	160	115

a) Using the data in the table, work out the half-life of iodine-131. [1]

b) Four months after the explosion, scientists were less concerned about the health risks from the iodine but were still worried about the effects from the caesium-137. Do you think they were right to be concerned? Explain your answer. [3]

Satellites and Gravity

A **satellite** is an object that **orbits** a planet in space. Satellites can be:

- **natural**, for example, the Moon
- **artificial** – they have been put in space by humans.

A satellite is kept in orbit by a **gravitational force**. **Gravity** is a universal force of attraction between masses. Gravity keeps:

- the planets orbiting the Sun
- the Moon orbiting the Earth.

Centripetal force acts towards the centre of a circle; it keeps an object moving in a circle. Gravity provides the centripetal force that keeps a satellite in orbit.

The weight of an object depends on the gravitational force on the surface of the planet.

Weight (N)	=	Mass (kg)	×	Gravitational field strength (N/kg)
w	=	m	×	g

On Earth, gravitational field strength, **g = 10N/kg**

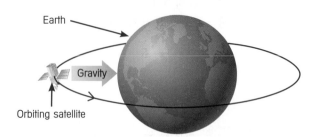

(HT) The gravitational force between two objects gets weaker as the objects are moved further apart. If the distance is doubled, the force drops to $\frac{1}{4}$. This is called the inverse square law.

Therefore, planets very close to the Sun experience a high gravitational force compared to planets that are further away.

The difference in gravitational force means that:

- planets closer to the Sun travel very quickly and have short orbital periods.
- planets further from the Sun travel very slowly and have long orbital periods.

Comets

Periodic comets orbit the Sun in almost-elliptical loops, unlike the planets, which have almost-circular orbits.

When a comet is close to the Sun it has to travel very fast to escape the gravitational force. When the comet is further away, it travels more slowly because the Sun's gravity pulls it back.

The effect is similar to a ball being thrown up into the air: it slows down as it gets higher and speeds up as it gets closer to the Earth.

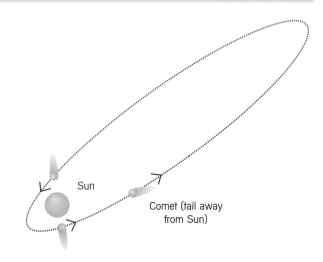

Artificial Satellites

Artificial satellites can orbit at different heights above the Earth's surface. A satellite's **orbital period** (the time it takes to make one complete orbit) increases with height above the Earth. The height at which a satellite orbits, and its period, determines what it can be used for.

Satellites in **low polar orbit**:
- travel very quickly
- go around the Earth several times each day.

Their uses include:
- imaging the Earth's surface
- weather forecasting
- military uses (e.g. spying).

Geostationary satellites:
- orbit much higher above the Earth
- take 24 hours to complete one orbit
- remain above a fixed position on the Earth's equator.

Their uses include:
- communications, for example, satellite television
- weather forecasting.

Satellites can also be used for scientific research and global positioning systems (GPS).

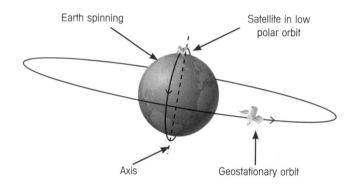

Earth spinning

Satellite in low polar orbit

Axis

Geostationary orbit

HT Orbits of Artificial Satellites

A satellite would naturally travel in a straight line. However, Earth's gravitational force causes it to continually accelerate towards Earth, and prevents it from flying off at a tangent.

The two effects balance, causing the satellite to remain in a circular orbit.

Artificial satellites in low polar orbit feel a strong gravitational force dragging them towards the Earth, so they travel faster than those in high orbits.

The speed of satellites in low orbit must be high enough to balance the gravitational force and keep them moving in a circle.

Geostationary satellites are in high orbits so the gravitational force on them is weak. They move more slowly and have further to travel.

Quick Test

1. Give an example of a natural satellite and an artificial satellite.
2. What happens to the speed of a comet as it travels past the Sun?
3. How long does it take for a geostationary satellite to orbit the Earth?

P5 Vectors and Equations of Motion

Scalar and Vector Quantities

Scalar quantities have a **size** only, for example:

- mass
- energy
- speed
- time.

Vector quantities have **size** and **direction**, for example:

- velocity
- force
- acceleration.

Speed

Speed is how fast an object is moving at a particular time. Direction isn't important when measuring **speed**. Speed is a scalar quantity.

The speed of an object can change during the course of its journey.

To calculate the **average speed** for a journey you can use the following equation:

$$\text{Average speed} = \frac{\text{Total distance}}{\text{Total time taken}}$$

Relative Speed

If two objects are moving near to each other, their motion is described in terms of their **relative speed**.

Direction is important when considering motion. Two cars travelling on a straight road will have a higher relative speed if they're moving towards each other than if they're travelling in the same direction.

Example 1

Car A and Car B are travelling towards each other on a straight road. Each car is travelling at 10m/s.

The relative speed of Car A and Car B is 20m/s. That is, if you're in Car A, it will look like Car B is travelling towards you at a speed of 20m/s.

Example 2

Car C and Car D are travelling in the same direction on a straight road. Car D is travelling at 8m/s and Car C is travelling at 10m/s. Every second, Car C will get 2m closer to Car D, which means that Car C's relative speed is 2m/s.

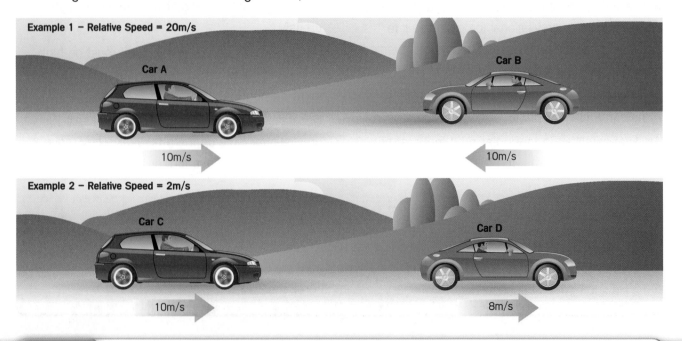

Example 1 – Relative Speed = 20m/s

Car A   Car B

10m/s   10m/s

Example 2 – Relative Speed = 2m/s

Car C   Car D

10m/s   8m/s

Key Words   Scalar quantity • Vector quantity • Speed • Relative speed

Velocity and Displacement

Velocity is an object's rate of **displacement** (change of distance) in a particular direction. You can calculate velocity and displacement using the following equations:

$$v = u + at$$

$$s = \left(\frac{u+v}{2}\right) \times t$$

where u = initial velocity, v = final velocity, a = acceleration, t = time, s = displacement.

Example

A bike travelling at 5m/s accelerates at 3m/s² for 5 seconds.

a) What is the bike's final velocity?

$$v = u + at$$

$$v = 5 + (3 \times 5) = \mathbf{20m/s}$$

b) How far did the bike travel whilst accelerating?

$$s = \left(\frac{u+v}{2}\right) \times t$$

$$s = \left(\frac{5+20}{2}\right) \times 5 = \mathbf{62.5m}$$

HT You can also calculate an object's final velocity, displacement, acceleration, or the time it was travelling for, by using the following equations:

$$v^2 = u^2 + 2as$$

$$s = ut + \frac{1}{2}at^2$$

Example 1

A runner starts a race and accelerates at 2.5m/s² for the first 20m of the race. What is the runner's final velocity?

$$v^2 = u^2 + 2as = 0^2 + (2 \times 2.5 \times 20) = 100$$

$$v = \sqrt{100} = \mathbf{10m/s}$$

Example 2

A car travelling at 20m/s accelerates at 3m/s² for 20 seconds. How far has the car travelled in this time?

$$s = ut + \tfrac{1}{2}at^2 = (20 \times 20) + (\tfrac{1}{2} \times 3 \times 20^2)$$

$$s = 400 + 600 = \mathbf{1000m}$$

Vectors

If two **forces** or velocities are **parallel**, it's possible to calculate their total effect from a **vector diagram**:

- Parallel vectors in the same direction add up:

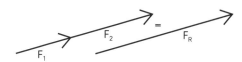

$$\boxed{F_R = F_1 + F_2}$$

- Parallel vectors in opposite directions subtract.

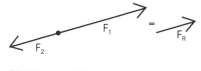

$$\boxed{F_R = F_1 - F_2}$$

HT If two forces or velocities are acting at **right angles** on the same object, you can work out the **resultant force/velocity** by using Pythagoras' theorem.

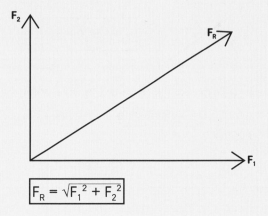

$$\boxed{F_R = \sqrt{F_1^2 + F_2^2}}$$

P5 Projectile Motion

Projectile Motion

When objects such as cannon balls or missiles are fired into the air they are called **projectiles**. When moving through the air, the following are all examples of projectiles:

- Golf balls
- Footballs
- Netballs
- Darts
- Long-jumpers.

The path that a projectile takes is known as its **trajectory**. If a projectile is launched horizontally on Earth, and there is no air resistance acting on it, the projectile will have:

- a constant **horizontal** velocity
- a steadily increasing vertical velocity.

The horizontal and vertical velocities are **vectors**. If air resistance is ignored, the only force acting on the projectile is **gravity**.

Earth's gravitational field causes the projectile to accelerate towards the ground, so it only affects the projectile's **vertical** velocity.

Because of the pull of gravity, objects projected horizontally on Earth follow a downward curving path, known as a **parabolic** trajectory.

The horizontal range depends only on the launch angle (measured from the horizontal). Footballs launched at 45° will travel the greatest distance.

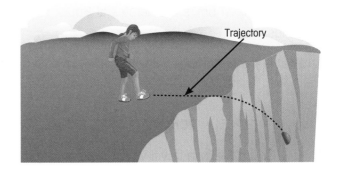

Trajectory

HT Calculating Projectile Velocity

The horizontal and vertical velocities of a projectile can be treated as separate vectors. Each vector has its own speed and direction.

The projectile's **resultant velocity** is the **vector sum** of the horizontal and vertical velocities.

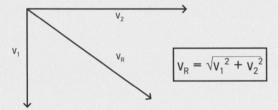

$$v_R = \sqrt{v_1^2 + v_2^2}$$

A projectile has **no** acceleration in the horizontal direction. This is because gravity only affects its vertical velocity.

You can use the velocity and displacement equations for objects that are projected horizontally above the Earth, where gravity is uniform.

Example

A stone is kicked off a cliff with a horizontal velocity of 3m/s. After 3 seconds, it lands in the sea 45m below. What is the **magnitude** (size) of the resultant velocity of the stone when it hits the sea?

Horizontally, the stone's velocity doesn't change.

Vertically, the stone's velocity increases from its initial velocity of 0m/s, due to gravity.

(Remember that acceleration due to gravity is 10m/s².)

$v = u + at = 0 + (10 \times 3) =$ **30m/s vertically**

To find the vector sum of the two velocities, use Pythagoras' theorem:

$v^2 = 3^2 + 30^2$

$v = \sqrt{909} =$ **30.1m/s**

Projectile • Trajectory • Gravity • Parabolic

Actions and Reactions

Every **action** has an equal and opposite **reaction**. When an object collides with another, or two bodies interact, they exert equal and opposite forces on each other. This is **Newton's Third Law of Motion**. For example, when you stand on solid ground:

- you exert a **force** on the ground (your weight)
- the ground exerts an equal and opposite force on you (contact force).

Gravity pulls you down towards the Earth and you are pulling the Earth towards you.

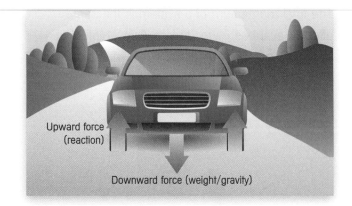

Upward force (reaction)

Downward force (weight/gravity)

Momentum

You can calculate **momentum** using this equation:

> **Momentum = Mass ✕ Velocity**

An increase in an object's mass and/or velocity will also increase its momentum.

Calculate the momentum of a person of mass 60kg travelling at 0.5m/s.

Momentum = Mass × Velocity

$$= 60 × 0.5$$

$$= \textbf{30kgm/s}$$

Collisions, Damage and Injury

In a **collision**, the velocities of the objects colliding are parallel.

If Object A hits Object B with a force, then Object B hits Object A with an equal force.

For example:

- if a lorry crashes into a car, then the car hits the lorry with the same force
- if a ball is hit with a racket, then the racket feels the same force from the ball and recoils.

Acceleration is the rate of change of an object's velocity over time. Many injuries in vehicle collisions, and sporting injuries, are caused by rapid acceleration (usually a sudden slowing down) of the body.

Safety features in vehicles reduce injury by spreading out the acceleration over a greater period of time. This means that the passenger's momentum is reduced more slowly.

(HT) During a collision, two objects exert an equal and opposite force on each other. You need to be able to calculate force, change in momentum, and time taken, using the following equation:

> $$\text{Force (N)} = \frac{\text{Change in momentum}}{\text{Time}}$$

Example

A boy of mass 50kg is walking at 2m/s (v_1). A gust of wind blows the boy forward for 2 seconds and he ends up running at 5m/s (v_2). What is the force of the wind?

$$\text{Force} = \frac{\text{Change in momentum}}{\text{Time}} = \frac{mv_2 - mv_1}{t}$$

$$= \frac{(50 × 5) - (50 × 2)}{2} = \frac{250 - 100}{2} = \textbf{75N}$$

Spreading a change in momentum over a longer time reduces:

- the forces required to act
- injuries caused by the forces.

P5 Action and Reaction

HT Conservation of Momentum

The total momentum of a system is the same after an event as it was before. Conservation of momentum is illustrated in the following table:

Example of Conservation of Momentum	Description
Recoil	The total momentum of a gun and bullet is zero. If the bullet is then fired, the total momentum is still zero. The bullet moves faster than the gun but it has a smaller mass, so their momenta are equal but acting in opposite directions, thus cancelling each other out.
Explosion	Before an explosion, the total momentum is zero. After an explosion, each fragment flies off in a different direction. The momentum of one fragment will cancel out the momentum of another fragment that's travelling in the opposite direction at the same momentum.
Rocket Propulsion	When a rocket's engines fire in space, the rocket speeds up, but the total momentum of the system is conserved. This is because the forward momentum of the rocket is cancelled out by the backward momentum of the gas it fires out.
Collision m_1 m_2 u_1 u_2	During a collision momentum is conserved. If two objects join (coalesce) during the collision, the momentum after the collision must equal the sum of their individual momentums. $$m_1 u_1 + m_2 u_2 = (m_1 + m_2) v$$ (where u and v are initial and final velocities/speeds)

Pressure

Gas particles are in constant motion. As particles collide with the walls of their container they exert a **force** on the wall. Force per unit area is called **pressure**.

The greater the number of collisions between the particles and the wall, the greater the pressure inside the container.

Pressure (Cont.)

If the gas particles are squashed into a smaller volume:

- the same number of particles will have less space to move in
- each particle will collide with the walls more frequently
- the pressure inside the container increases.

If the temperature of the gas is increased:

- the particles gain energy
- with increased kinetic energy, the particles move more quickly
- each particle will collide with the wall more frequently and collide with more force
- the pressure inside the container increases.

(HT) As a particle strikes the wall of its container, it undergoes a change in its momentum. This produces a force on the wall.

The size of this force depends upon the length of time that the particle is in contact with the wall (time taken).

$$\text{Force} = \frac{\text{Change in momentum}}{\text{Time taken}}$$

Rockets

At launch, a rocket requires a large force to enable it to accelerate. This force is provided by the exhaust gases. The force pushing the gas backwards out of the exhaust equals the forward force of the gas on the rocket.

The fast-moving particles in the gas collide with the walls of the rocket. This produces a force on the rocket.

(HT) Rockets used to launch satellites into orbit require very large forces to lift both the rocket and the satellite. Sufficient force is achieved by:

- a large number of particles of exhaust gas
- the particles moving at high speed.

Quick Test

1. List two examples of scalar quantities and two examples of vector quantities.
2. State the equation used to calculate momentum.
3. (HT) What is the result of spreading the change in momentum during a collision over a longer time?

P5 Satellite Communication

Radio Waves

Radio waves have a very long wavelength (1m–10km). Different **frequencies** of **radio waves** are affected by the Earth's atmosphere in different ways:

1. Some frequencies (between 30MHz and 30GHz) pass through the Earth's atmosphere (relatively short wavelength).
2. Some frequencies (above 30GHz) are reduced in strength, or even stopped, by the Earth's atmosphere. They are **absorbed** and **scattered** by rain, dust and other atmospheric effects.
3. Some frequencies (below 30MHz) are reflected by a part of the Earth's upper atmosphere called the **ionosphere**.

The same frequencies can't be used to send information to all types of satellite. Low orbiting satellites use low frequency signals. Geostationary satellites are much further above the Earth so they need to use high frequency signals.

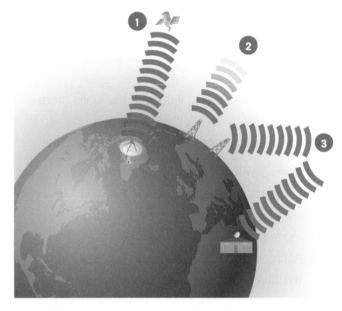

Microwaves have a higher frequency, and shorter **wavelength**, than radio waves. They are used to transmit information to orbiting artificial satellites, which then retransmit information back to Earth.

Diffraction

When a wave meets an obstacle, such as a hill, it will spread around the hill. If it meets a gap, it spreads out through the gap. This can cause the wave to be **diffracted**, i.e. spread out from the edges.

Different sized gaps cause different amounts of diffraction.

For example, if you stand in a room with the door open, you can hear sounds from outside the room.

This is because the wavelength of sound is about the same size as a doorway, so the sound waves spread out as they come through the door.

(HT) The amount a wave is diffracted depends on the size of the gap and the wavelength of the wave:
- Large gaps allow waves to pass straight through without diffracting.
- Diffraction is most obvious when the size of the gap is equal to the wavelength.

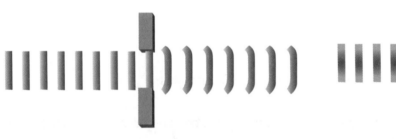

Gap larger than wavelength – slight diffraction

Gap same size as wavelength – increased diffraction

HT Diffraction of Radio Waves

Diffraction makes radio waves useful for television and radio broadcasts because, by spreading out, the waves can effectively get around obstacles.

Owing to their very long **wavelengths**, it's relatively easy for radio waves to diffract around obstacles and the horizon. This means that long wavelength radio waves have a very long **range**.

The size of an aerial dish used to receive microwaves must be much larger than the wavelength of those microwaves. This produces very little diffraction of the waves.

When a long wavelength radio wave encounters a hill, the points on the wavefront near the hill set off new waves. These waves are curved, which is why the wave begins to spread round the hill.

Microwaves have a short wavelength, so they don't diffract much around large obstacles. This is why microwaves are only sent in thin beams when transmitting information.

This means that the receiving dish and satellite must be in exact alignment.

The receiving dish and the transmitter must be in exact alignment.

Receiving Programmes

Special equipment is needed to receive radio and television programmes. An aerial, such as a metal rod, can be used to pick up a radio signal.

A satellite signal can only be picked up using a 'dish'. The dish is curved to focus all the microwaves onto the receiver at its centre.

Quick Test

1. What is the typical wavelength of radio waves?
2. What effect can the Earth's atmosphere have on radio waves above 30GHz?
3. Why are radio waves refracted as they pass through the ionosphere?
4. HT Why do radio waves, but not microwaves, easily diffract around hills?

P5 Nature of Waves

How Light Travels

Light, like all **electromagnetic waves**, is a transverse wave and travels in straight lines. As a result, you see sharp-edged shadows and a solar eclipse when the Moon passes between the Sun and the Earth.

Diffraction and **refraction** can make light look as though it bends.

When light is diffracted, the diffracted waves behave like separate beams of light, and can overlap one another.

Interference

When two waves overlap, it causes **interference**. Interference produces areas of:

- **reinforcement** (where waves add together):

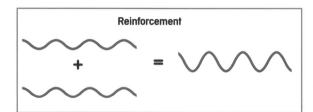

Reinforcement

- **cancellation** (where waves subtract from each other):

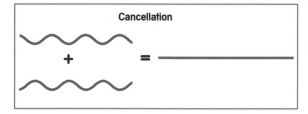

Cancellation

For example, when water waves overlap:
- areas of reinforcement are where the ripples are deeper, because their height is made up of two ripples added together.
- areas of cancellation are where the water's surface is flat, because the peak of one wave fills in the trough of the other.

	Effect of Reinforcement	Effect of Cancellation
Sound waves	Loud areas	Quiet areas
Light waves	Bright areas	Dark areas

A stable interference pattern is only produced when the wave sources are **coherent** (have the same frequency), so light sources are **monochromatic**. Interference patterns are evidence for the wave nature of light.

(HT) Coherent wave sources:
- have the same frequency
- are in phase
- have the same amplitude.

Constructive interference (reinforcement) occurs when identical waves arrive **in phase** at a point. This produces a wave with larger amplitude, so you see bright fringes.

Destructive interference (cancellation) occurs when identical waves arrive **out of phase**. The amplitude of the resulting wave is zero, so you see dark fringes.

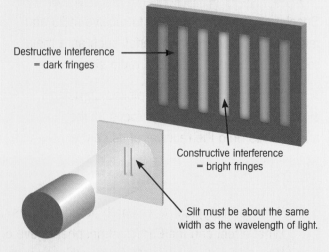

Destructive interference = dark fringes

Constructive interference = bright fringes

Slit must be about the same width as the wavelength of light.

Replacing the double slit with a single slit results in a pattern with a much brighter central fringe.

(HT) Path Difference

Even though two waves come from the same source, they may have taken different paths to reach an object.

For example, one wave could have reflected off a mirror while the other could have taken a direct path to the object.

If two waves have arrived at a point by different paths, then the **path difference** needs to be calculated. The path difference is:

- an **odd** number of half wavelengths for **destructive interference**
- an **even** number of half wavelengths for **constructive interference**.

Polarisation

Light waves are **electromagnetic**. All electromagnetic waves are **transverse waves**. This means that the **oscillation** of a wave is at 90° to the direction that the wave is travelling.

Only transverse waves can be **plane polarised**. That is, if a material is a horizontal polariser:

- only horizontal oscillations can get through
- other oscillations are absorbed.

Polarisation is used in some sunglasses to reduce glare from sunlight. The light that gets through the sunglasses is plane polarised and, therefore, less bright.

When light is incident on water, the reflected light is *partly* plane polarised.

Polarising lenses work by absorbing light that's reflected off shiny surfaces (such as water), which have oscillations in certain directions.

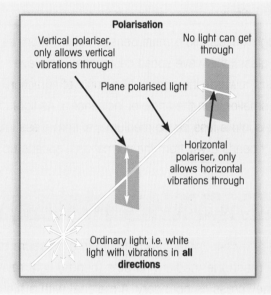

Polarisation

Vertical polariser, only allows vertical vibrations through

No light can get through

Plane polarised light

Horizontal polariser, only allows horizontal vibrations through

Ordinary light, i.e. white light with vibrations in **all directions**

Light – Wave or Particle?

There are two main theories about the nature of light.

During the 17th century, many scientists believed that light behaved like a **particle**. Light travels in straight lines and does not bend around objects. Because of this we observe shadows. Waves are able to bend around objects, so light couldn't be a wave. Reflection can be described in terms of light behaving like a particle. As light strikes a surface it

exerts a pressure on the surface (very much like a ball hitting a wall).

But the particle model wasn't universally accepted amongst scientists. Scientists opposing this view believed that light is a series of **waves**. This theory was supported by experiments demonstrating diffraction of waves, interference and dispersion (splitting white light into a spectrum).

P5 Refraction of Waves

Refraction

A **medium** is a substance that waves can travel through.

A line at 90° to the surface of a medium is known as the **normal**. When light travels from one medium to another at an angle to the normal it changes direction. This is **refraction**.

Refraction occurs at the boundary between two media due to a change in the wave speed as it travels through the different densities.

The angle at which the light ray travels through the second medium is the **angle of refraction**, **r**. This depends on the angle at which the light hits the boundary between the media, that is, the **angle of incidence**, **i**.

As light travels into a more dense medium (from air into glass), the wave speed decreases. The wave 'bends' towards the normal. The angle of refraction, r, is smaller than the angle of incidence, i. As light travels into a less dense medium (i.e. from glass into air), it bends away from the normal as it speeds up.

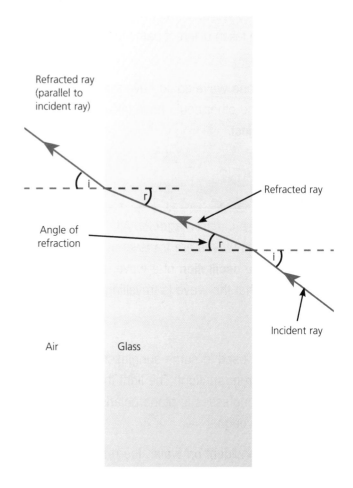

Refractive Index

The **refractive index** of a medium is a measure of how much the medium refracts (bends) light rays as they cross its boundary. A material with a higher refractive index produces a greater degree of bending.

The amount of refraction increases when there's a greater change in the light's wave speed as it passes from one medium to another.

The refractive index, **n**, can be calculated by comparing the speed of light in the medium with the fastest speed that light can travel (i.e. in a vacuum):

Materials with higher refractive indices have a smaller critical angle.

Material	Refractive Index	Critical Angles (degrees)
Water	1.33	48.8
Glass	1.50	41.8
Diamond	2.42	24.4

$$\text{Refractive index, n} = \frac{\text{Speed of light in a vacuum}}{\text{Speed of light in a medium}}$$

HT Refractive Index (Cont.)

Diamond has a high refractive index. All light incident on the diamond–air boundary at an angle greater than 24.4 degrees will undergo **total internal reflection (TIR)**.

This is what produces the sparkling effect of diamonds.

Critical Angle

The **critical angle** is the maximum angle of incidence (measured from the normal) before **total internal reflection** (TIR) occurs. Different media have different critical angles.

Not all light is refracted when it leaves glass or water to travel through air. Some of the light is reflected from the surface:

1 If the angle of incidence is **less than** the critical angle, most of the light is refracted into the air.

2 If light hits the boundary at **exactly** the critical angle, it undergoes maximum refraction, emerging at 90° to the normal.

3 If the angle of incidence is **larger than** the critical angle, no light is refracted, i.e. all the light is **reflected** back into the medium. This is known as **total internal reflection**.

Different media (materials) have different critical angles.

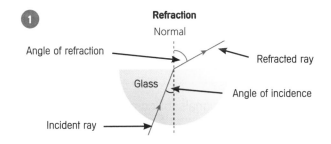

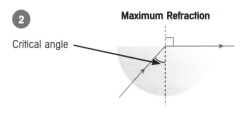

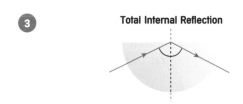

HT Total internal reflection relies on light being refracted away from the normal as the light ray speeds up. Therefore, total internal reflection only occurs when:

- light travels from a medium with a high refractive index into a medium with a lower refractive index
- the angle of incidence is more than the critical angle.

The higher a medium's refractive index, the lower its critical angle. The critical angle, **c**, can be calculated using the following equation:

$$\sin c = \frac{n_r}{n_i}$$

Where: n_r = refractive index of air
n_i = refractive index of medium

P5 Refraction of Waves

Uses of Total Internal Reflection

Uses of total internal reflection include optical fibres and bike reflectors.

Optical Fibres

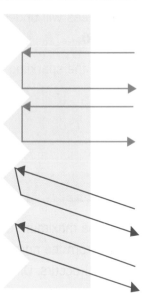

Light incident on the glass–air boundary at an angle greater than the critical angle is reflected (TIR). In this way, light travels down the length of the fibre optic cable.

Fibre optics are used:
* to send digital signals for communication
* in endoscopes to observe tissues inside the body.

Bike Reflectors

The light undergoes total internal reflection at the plastic–air boundary and leaves the reflector parallel to the ray of light entering.

Dispersion

Light is made up of the colours of the **spectrum**. All of the colours travel at the same speed in a vacuum, but at different speeds in other media.

When light travels through a prism it's slowed down, and therefore refracted.

Different colours refract by different amounts:
* Blue/violet light is slowed down the most.
* Red light is slowed down the least.

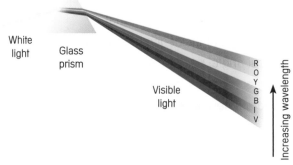

This means that blue light is **deviated** (changes direction) more than red light. This is **dispersion**.

(HT) The spectral colours have different wavelengths, which is why they are slowed down by different amounts when they travel through a prism.

The colours that have shorter wavelengths are slowed and deviated more than the colours that have longer wavelengths. Therefore, glass has a higher refractive index for the colours that have shorter wavelengths. Blue light has a greater refractive index than red light.

Convex Lenses

A **convex lens** is a **converging** lens. When light rays pass through it they meet at a focus.

The **focal length** is the distance between the **centre** of the lens and the **focal point** (focus). Fatter lenses refract light more so they have shorter focal lengths.

Light passing through the optical centre is not refracted. If a beam of light **parallel** to the axis passes through a convex lens, it will pass through the focal point. If a **diverging** beam of light passes through a convex lens, the light will converge but will not hit the focal point. Convex lenses can be used as magnifying glasses, in cameras, projectors and some spectacles.

In cameras and projectors, light passes through the convex lens and converges to create a **real image** on a screen. For the image to be in focus, the lens has to be moved so that the image forms on the screen where the rays from a particular point on the object meet at a point on the screen.

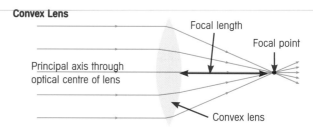

Convex Lens

Focal length

Focal point

Principal axis through optical centre of lens

Convex lens

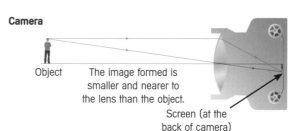

Camera

Object

The image formed is smaller and nearer to the lens than the object.

Screen (at the back of camera)

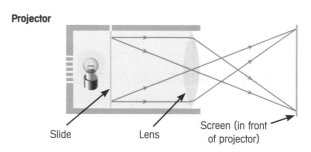

Projector

Slide

Lens

Screen (in front of projector)

(HT) **Real images** can be projected onto a screen and are always **inverted** (upside down). Virtual images are the right way up, but they can't be projected onto a screen.

Ray diagrams can be drawn to work out the position and size of an image formed by a convex lens:

1. Draw a ray from the bottom of the object (O), parallel to the axis, through the centre of the lens.
2. Draw a ray from the top of the object through the centre of the lens.

3. Draw another ray from the top of the object (O), this time parallel to the axis and only as far as the lens. Continue the ray from the lens so that it passes through the focal point (F).
4. The point at which the rays join is the top of the image (I).

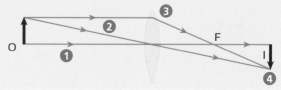

Magnification

Magnification is a measure of how much bigger the image is than the object:

$$\text{Magnification} = \frac{\text{Image size}}{\text{Object size}}$$

Quick Test

1. What is the focal length?
2. Which colour of the spectrum is refracted the most as it passes into a prism?

P5 Exam Practice Questions

1 Satellites are objects that orbit planets in space. They can be natural or artificial.

   a) Which of the following options is not a use of a satellite in low polar orbit? Tick (✓) the correct option. **[1]**

       A Weather forecasting ☐   **B** GPS ☐

       C Spying ☐   **D** Imaging the Earth's surface ☐

   b) Describe the orbit of a geostationary satellite. **[2]**

2 Suhaib is driving his new car.

   a) The first time he goes out, he takes 10 minutes to travel 6km. What is his average speed in m/s? **[2]**

   b) A few days later Suhaib drives his new car to his friend's house. He travels at 70km/h and overtakes a car travelling at 60km/h. What is his relative speed? **[1]**

   c) Is speed a scalar or a vector quantity? Explain your answer. **[1]**

3 **a)** Elaine kicks a ball horizontally off the edge of a cliff. Describe what happens to the projectile's velocity in the horizontal direction and in the vertical direction as it falls. **[2]**

     Horizontal

     Vertical

   b) The ball has an initial horizontal velocity of 6m/s. It hits the ground 18m from the base of the cliff. Calculate the time it took the ball to reach the ground. **[2]**

   c) The initial vertical velocity of the ball was 0m/s. Calculate the height of the cliff (using $g = 10m/s^2$). **[3]**

4 Lucy's horse, Darcy, has a mass of 200kg. Lucy has a mass of 50kg. Lucy takes Darcy out riding and they gallop at 30m/s. What is the total momentum? **[2]**

5 A student shines a ray of light through a glass block, as in the diagram shown.

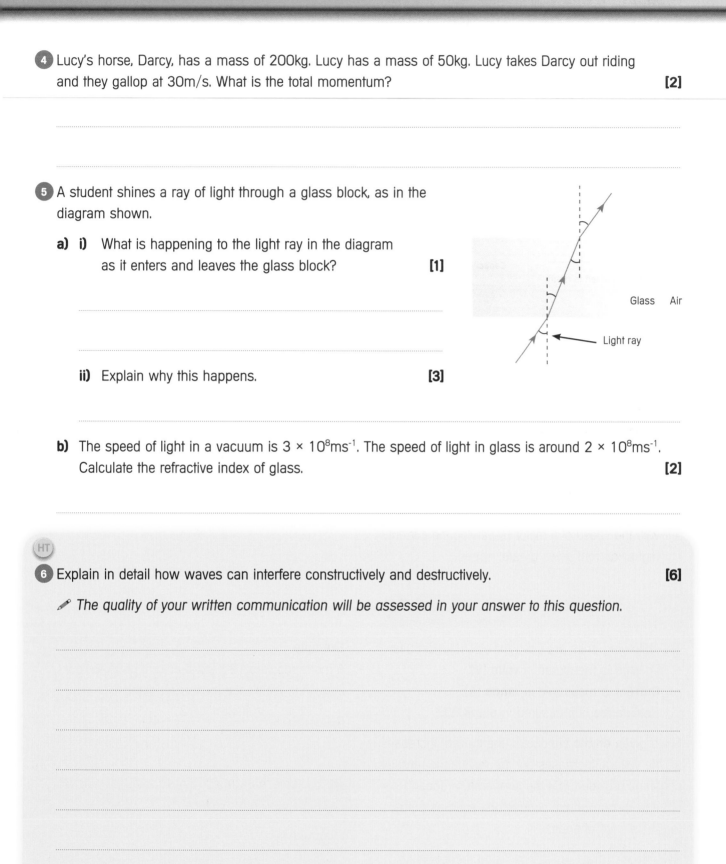

Glass   Air

Light ray

a) **i)** What is happening to the light ray in the diagram as it enters and leaves the glass block? **[1]**

ii) Explain why this happens. **[3]**

b) The speed of light in a vacuum is $3 \times 10^8 \text{ms}^{-1}$. The speed of light in glass is around $2 \times 10^8 \text{ms}^{-1}$. Calculate the refractive index of glass. **[2]**

HT

6 Explain in detail how waves can interfere constructively and destructively. **[6]**

✎ *The quality of your written communication will be assessed in your answer to this question.*

P6 Resisting

Circuit Symbols

The following **symbols** are used to represent components in a circuit:

Fixed resistor		Battery		Cell		Power supply	(DC) (AC)
Variable resistor		Switch (open)		Relay	NO COM NC	Bulb	
Diode (current flowing left to right)		Capacitor		Thermistor		LDR	

Resistors

A **resistor** in a circuit resists the flow of current.

A **variable resistor** (rheostat) can have its resistance changed. It can be used to:

- control current – increasing the resistance results in a lower current
- vary the brightness of a bulb by varying the current – higher current gives a brighter bulb
- vary the speed of a motor by varying the current – higher current gives greater speed.

HT The resistance of a variable resistor (rheostat) is altered by changing the length of the wire. A longer wire creates a higher resistance.

Variable Resistor used in Dimmer Switch

Ohm's Law

The following units are used for electrical circuits:

- Voltage is measured in **volts** (**V**).
- **Current** is measured in **amps** (**A**).
- **Resistance** is measured in **ohms** (Ω).

For a given **ohmic** conductor, the current increases as the voltage increases but the resistance remains constant, provided that the temperature doesn't change. In non-ohmic conductors, such as bulbs, the resistance changes.

You can calculate resistance using the following equation:

$$\text{Resistance } (\Omega) = \frac{\text{Voltage (V)}}{\text{Current (A)}}$$

Example

A motor requires 12V and a current of 3A to flow through it. What's the motor's resistance?

$$\text{Resistance} = \frac{\text{Voltage}}{\text{Current}} = \frac{12}{3} = \textbf{4}\Omega$$

HT You can rearrange the resistance formula to calculate current or voltage.

Example

Calculate the current in a kettle if the voltage is 230V and the resistance of the heating element is 20Ω.

$$\text{Current} = \frac{\text{Voltage}}{\text{Resistance}} = \frac{230}{20} = \textbf{11.5A}$$

Current • Resistance • Voltage

Voltage–Current Graphs

The voltage–current graph for an **ohmic conductor** is a straight line. The **gradient** of the graph shows the resistance of the conductor. The steeper the gradient, the higher the resistance.

HT To work out the resistance of an ohmic conductor from a V–I graph, use the following formula:

$$\text{Resistance } (\Omega) = \frac{\text{Change in Voltage (V)}}{\text{Change in Current (A)}}$$

The voltage–current graph for a **non-ohmic conductor** (for example, a bulb) is a curve. The **increasing gradient** shows that the resistance increases as the current increases.

When a wire gets hot, its resistance increases. This means that the hotter a wire gets, the lower the current that can flow through it.

HT As the temperature of a resistor rises, its resistance increases. This is why the V–I graph for a filament bulb is curved. The curve shows an increase in gradient as the current rises, showing that the resistance is increasing.

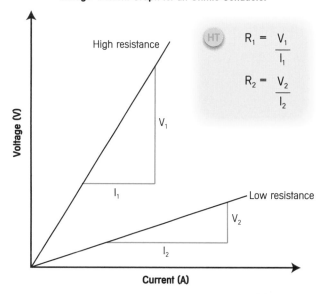

Voltage–Current Graph for an Ohmic Conductor

$$R_1 = \frac{V_1}{I_1}$$

$$R_2 = \frac{V_2}{I_2}$$

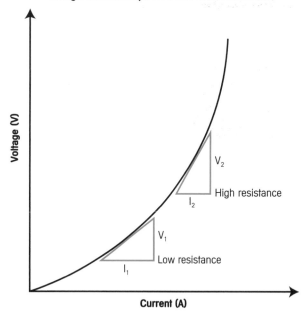

Voltage–Current Graph for a Non-Ohmic Conductor

Resistance

An electric current is the flow of charge carriers through a material. In metals the charge carriers are electrons.

As electrons pass along a wire, they collide with atoms (ions) in the metal. This causes the atoms to vibrate more.

As a result:

- the number of collisions increases
- the resistance in the wire increases
- the temperature of the wire increases.

P6 Sharing

Resistors in Series

Two or more resistors in series will increase the overall resistance of the circuit.

The total resistance, R_T, of the circuit can be found by simply **adding** the individual resistances together.

$$R_T = R_1 + R_2 + R_3$$

Example

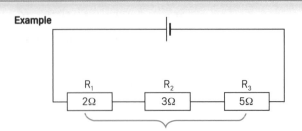

In this example the total resistance, $R_T = R_1 + R_2 + R_3$

$$R_T = 2 + 3 + 5$$
$$= 10\Omega$$

Resistors In Parallel

Resistors in parallel **reduce** the overall resistance of a circuit.

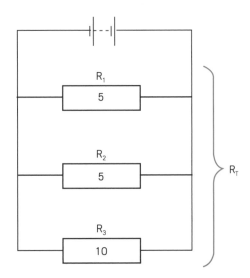

HT The total resistance, R_T, of resistors in parallel is calculated using the following equation:

$$\frac{1}{R_T} = \frac{1}{R_1} + \frac{1}{R_2} + \frac{1}{R_2}$$

In this example the total resistance, R_T, of the circuit is:

$$\frac{1}{R_T} = \frac{1}{5} + \frac{1}{5} + \frac{1}{10}$$

$$= \frac{2}{10} + \frac{2}{10} + \frac{1}{10} = \frac{5}{10}$$

Remember that this value is $\frac{1}{R_T}$, so the answer must be inverted:

$$\frac{1}{R_T} = \frac{10}{5} = 2\Omega$$

Potential Dividers

A **potential divider** can be made of **fixed resistors** that are arranged to produce a required **voltage**, or potential difference (pd).

1 In this example, there is a pd across each of the two fixed resistors. If a connection is made across one of the fixed resistors, the pd across that resistor is the output voltage.

2 If a **variable resistor** is used in the potential divider, the exact pd of the output from the circuit can be chosen. The lower the resistance, the lower the pd.

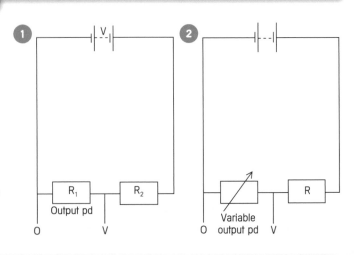

Key Words   **Potential difference**

If the value of resistor R_2 is much greater than R_1, then the output at Pd will be approximately V (the input Pd).

If the value of resistor R_2 is much less than R_1, then the output Pd across R_1 will be almost zero.

If R_1 and R_2 are both replaced by a variable resistor, then the threshold of the output voltage can be adjusted.

The output pd from a potential divider can be calculated using the following equation:

$$\text{Output pd, } V_{out} = \frac{R_1}{(R_1 + R_2)} \times V_{in}$$

Example

A 20Ω resistor and a 30Ω resistor are connected in series with a 100V supply to make a potential divider. What is the output across the 20Ω resistor?

$$V_{out} = \frac{20}{20 + 30} \times 100$$
$$= 0.4 \times 100 = \textbf{40V}$$

Using a variable resistor in place of a fixed resistor will give an output pd that can be **adjusted** to provide the voltage required to operate the chosen device.

The voltage can range from zero to almost the total voltage of the circuit.

LDRs and Thermistors

A **light dependent resistor** (**LDR**) changes its resistance in response to different light levels:
- Bright light causes lower resistance.
- Dim light causes higher resistance.

A **thermistor** changes its resistance when the temperature changes:
- High temperature causes lower resistance.
- Low temperature causes higher resistance.

HT Using an LDR in place of a fixed resistor in a potential divider gives an output voltage that depends upon light conditions. For example, bright light causes low output voltage because the resistance of the LDR is lower than the fixed resistor. In dim light, the output voltage is high.

Using a thermistor as the variable resistor in a potential divider gives an output voltage that depends upon the temperature. For example, a higher temperature causes a lower output voltage because the resistance of the thermistor is lower than the fixed resistor.

Quick Test

1 What happens to the resistance of a resistor as its temperature increases?
2 Which combination of two identical resistors has the greatest resistance – series or parallel?
3 What happens to the resistance of an LDR in bright light?

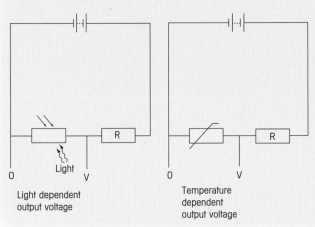

Light dependent output voltage

Temperature dependent output voltage

Transistors

The **transistor** is the basic building block of many electrical devices. It is an electronic switch.

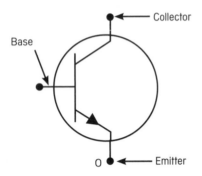

A small base current (I_b) is used to switch on a larger current, which flows through the collector (I_c) and emitter (I_e).

$$I_e = I_c + I_b$$

Millions of these tiny transistors are used in computers and other electrical equipment to speed up processing. They can be connected together to work like **logic gates**.

The two transistors connected together in this circuit produce the same output as an AND gate.

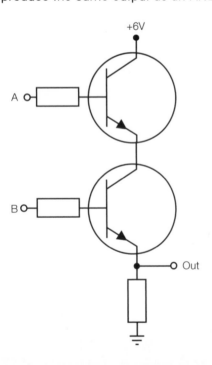

Increasing miniaturisation (making the transistors smaller):
- increases the number of transistors that can be connected in a processor
- means computer processors can be made smaller.

Two factors affect how small transistors can become:
- Smaller components dissipate more heat as a current passes through them.
- As transistors become thinner, they offer less resistance to the electrons due to '**quantum tunnelling**'.

HT An **npn transistor** can be used as a switch for an LED.

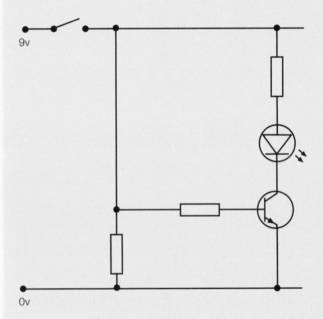

When the switch is closed, a current flows through resistor A to the base. The transistor then allows a current to flow (through the collector and emitter) from +9v to 0v. The LED turns on. Resistors protect the transistor.

A high voltage or current through the transistor will damage the transistor.

Inputs and Logic Gates

The input to a logic gate can be:
- a high voltage (about 5V) – called **high**, 1
- a low voltage (about 0V) – called **low**, 0.

The output (Q) of a logic gate is either high or low, depending on its input signal(s).

Switches, LDRs and thermistors can be used in series with fixed resistors to provide input signals for logic gates. In this case, they are being made into potential dividers. A pd, which can be either high (1) or low (0), is fed to the input.

Gate	Truth Table		
NOT gate – gives out the **opposite** of the input. A ——▷o—— Q	**A**		**Q**
	0		1
	1		0
AND gate – gives a high output if the input on Input A **and** Input B are high. A —— B —— Q	**A**	**B**	**Q**
	0	0	0
	0	1	0
	1	0	0
	1	1	1
OR gate – gives a high output if Input A **or** Input B is high. A —— B —— Q	**A**	**B**	**Q**
	0	0	0
	0	1	1
	1	0	1
	1	1	1
NAND gate – an AND gate and a NOT gate in series; the output is the **opposite of an AND** gate. A —— B —— Q	**A**	**B**	**Q**
	0	0	1
	0	1	1
	1	0	1
	1	1	0
NOR gate – an OR gate and a NOT gate in series; the output is the **opposite of an OR** gate. A —— B —— Q	**A**	**B**	**Q**
	0	0	1
	0	1	0
	1	0	0
	1	1	0

P6 Even More Logical

Thermistors as Inputs for Logic Gates

When a **thermistor** and a fixed resistor are connected in series, a variable potential divider can be produced. This can provide the input to a logic gate that depends upon **temperature**.

(HT) If the fixed resistor is changed to a variable resistor, the temperature at which the logic gate receives the high input can be set. The voltage output across the variable resistor provides a signal with adjustable threshold voltage to the logic gate.

The example shows a heater control circuit. When the temperature falls, the **resistance** of the thermistor is high. This gives a high input to the AND gate, so the heater is switched on.

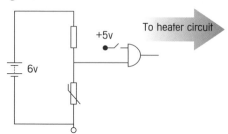

LDRs as Inputs for Logic Gates

When an **LDR** is connected in series to a fixed resistor, it produces a device that can provide the input to a logic gate that depends upon **light conditions**.

The example shows a lighting control circuit. In the dark, the resistance of the LDR is high. This means that the pd on the input of the AND gate is high, so the light switches on.

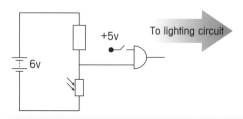

(HT) If the fixed resistor is changed to a variable resistor, the light level at which the logic gate receives the high input can be set.

LEDs as Outputs

The output from a logic gate can switch on a **light emitting diode** (**LED**). When the logic gate gives a high output, the LED lights up. This could be used to show, for example, when a heater comes on.

(HT) An LED can be used to indicate the output of a logic gate because it emits light when a voltage is fed to it. An LED only requires a very small current. A resistor is put in series with the LED to ensure that the current flowing through it isn't too large.

Latches and Relays

A **relay** can be used as a switch. A small current in the relay coil switches on a circuit in which a larger current flows.

(HT) A **relay** is needed in order for a logic gate to switch on a current in a mains circuit, because:
* a logic gate has a low power output (whereas the mains has a higher power).
* the relay isolates the low voltage from the high voltage mains.

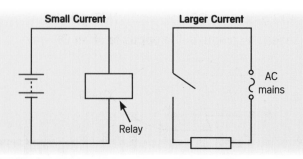

Key Words   Resistance • Relay

Complex Truth Tables

You need to be able to complete a truth table for a logic system with up to three inputs made from logic gates, in order to work out what the final output is.

For example, the following diagram and truth table show a logic system consisting of an AND gate connected to an OR gate.

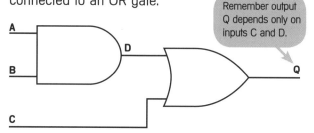

Remember output Q depends only on inputs C and D.

A	B	C	D	Q
0	0	0	0	0
0	0	1	0	1
0	1	0	0	0
0	1	1	0	1
1	0	0	0	0
1	0	1	0	1
1	1	0	1	1
1	1	1	1	1

(HT) In your exam you may be asked to work through the truth table of a logic system with up to four inputs made from logic gates:

1. Set up the inputs, (A, B, C, D, etc.) and then fill in the truth table using **binary**.
2. Work out the output for a logic gate for each pair of inputs.
3. Repeat the process for each logic gate until the final outputs have been found.

The following example is for a logic system consisting of an OR gate and an AND gate connected to a NOR gate.

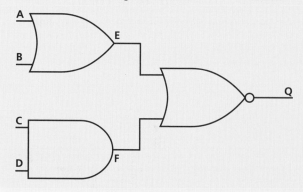

A	B	C	D	E	F	Q
0	0	0	0	0	0	1
0	0	0	1	0	0	1
0	0	1	0	0	0	1
0	0	1	1	0	1	0
0	1	0	0	1	0	0
0	1	0	1	1	0	0
0	1	1	0	1	0	0
0	1	1	1	1	1	0
1	0	0	0	1	0	0
1	0	0	1	1	0	0
1	0	1	0	1	0	0
1	0	1	1	1	1	0
1	1	0	0	1	0	0
1	1	0	1	1	0	0
1	1	1	0	1	0	0
1	1	1	1	1	1	0

Quick Test

1. What value must both inputs to an AND gate have so that the output is high?
2. (HT) What is the job of a relay?
3. (HT) Which gate can be used in place of a NOT and an OR gate together?

P6 Motoring

Magnetic Field Around a Wire

A straight wire carrying an electric current has a circular **magnetic field** around it. The magnetic field is made up of **concentric circles**.

If the wire is put near a magnet, the two magnetic fields interact and the wire can move.

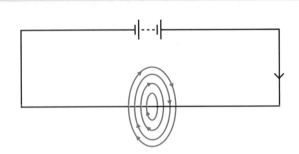

Magnetic Field Around Coils

The magnetic field around a **rectangular coil** forms straight lines through the centre of the coil:

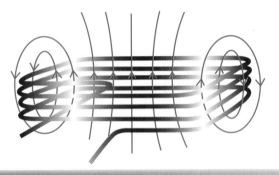

The magnetic field around a **solenoid** looks like the magnetic field around a bar magnet:

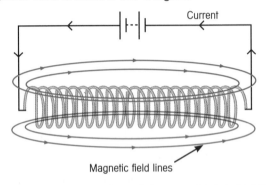

Magnetic field lines

Wires Moving in Magnetic Fields

If a current-carrying wire is placed in a magnetic field it experiences a force and moves. This is called the **motor effect**.

For a current-carrying wire in a magnetic field to experience the maximum **force**, it has to be at **right angles** to the magnetic field.

The direction the wire moves in depends upon:
- the direction of the current
- the direction of the magnetic field.

The direction the wire moves in can be reversed by:
- reversing the direction of the current
- reversing the direction of the magnetic field.

HT Fleming's Left Hand Rule

Fleming's Left Hand Rule can be used to predict the direction of the force on a current-carrying wire.

The rule states that if:
- your first finger points in the direction of the magnetic field, N to S, **and**
- your second finger points in the direction of the current, + to −, **then**
- your thumb will point in the direction of the force on the wire.

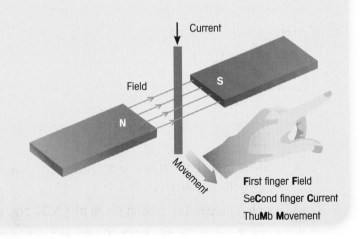

First finger **F**ield
Se**C**ond finger **C**urrent
Thu**M**b **M**ovement

Key Words   **Magnetic field • Force • Fleming's Left Hand Rule**

Coils Rotating in Magnetic Fields

A simple **direct current** (**DC**) electric **motor** works by using a current-carrying coil.

When a current-carrying coil is placed in a magnetic field, it will **rotate** in the following way:

1. The current flowing through the coil creates a magnetic field.
2. The magnetic field of the magnet and the magnetic field of the coil interact.
3. Each side of the coil experiences a force in an opposite direction because the current is flowing in opposite directions in the two parts of the coil.
4. The forces combine to make the coil rotate.

Electric motors transfer energy to the device (load). Some energy is wasted to the surroundings, often as heat.

Electric motors are found in many devices, such as:
- washing machines
- CD players
- food processors
- electric drills and electric lawnmowers
- windscreen wipers.

The speed of a motor can be increased by:
- increasing the size of the electric current
- increasing the number of turns on the coil
- increasing the strength of the magnetic field.

(HT) The direction of the current affects the direction of the force on the motor coil.

The current must always flow in the same direction (DC) relative to the magnet in order to keep the coil rotating.

This is achieved by using a **split-ring commutator**.

A split-ring commutator changes the direction of the current in the coil every half turn.

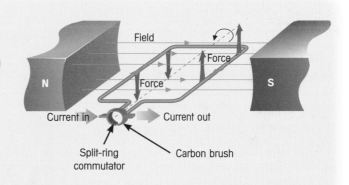

Field

Force

Force

N

S

Current in   Current out

Split-ring
commutator   Carbon brush

Radial Fields

Because the maximum force is produced when the coil and the magnetic field are at right angles, curved pole pieces are used to give a **radial field**.

The effect of the radial field is that the magnetic field lines and the coil are always at the correct angle to give maximum force.

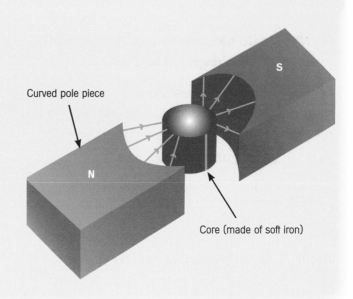

Curved pole piece

S

N

Core (made of soft iron)

P6 Generating

Generating Electricity

Generating electricity is known as the **dynamo effect**. Electricity can be generated by moving a wire near a magnet, or a magnet near a wire.

In the UK, mains electricity is generated at 50 hertz (50Hz). This means the current goes back and forth along the wire 50 times each second.

DC Generator

A DC generator is a DC motor working in reverse. Instead of feeding a voltage to the coil and watching it move, the coil is moved to produce a voltage.

N.B. You'll need to be able to label the diagram of a DC generator (opposite) in the exam.

A DC generator enables energy to be stored for later use.

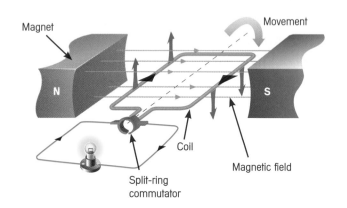

Magnet

Movement

N

S

Coil

Magnetic field

Split-ring commutator

AC Generator

An **alternating current (AC)** can be generated by rotating a magnet inside a coil of wire.

In a power station, the electricity is generated by rotating electromagnets inside coils of wire.

(HT) Where a DC generator has commutators, an AC generator has **slip rings** and **brushes**.

As the wire moves up (past the north pole of the magnet) a current is induced in the wire. After the coil has turned half a turn this section of wire will be moving down past the south pole.

A current is now induced in the wire in the opposite direction. This means that the induced current is an alternating current (AC).

This is how an AC generator ensures that the current changes direction every half cycle.

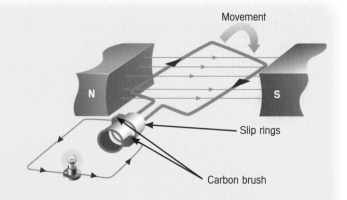

Movement

N

S

Slip rings

Carbon brush

N.B. The brushes make contact with the slip rings, enabling the current to flow while the coil is rotating freely.

Dynamo effect • Alternating current

Inducing Voltages

A **voltage** is induced:

- across a **wire**, when the wire moves relative to a magnetic field
- across a **coil**, when the magnetic field linking the coil changes.

Reversing the direction of the changing magnetic field also changes the direction of the induced voltage.

The voltage induced can be increased, as shown in the table.

(HT) The induced voltage depends upon the rate at which the magnetic field changes.

The rate of change of the magnetic field can be increased by increasing the speed of movement.

1 increasing the speed at which the magnet or coil moves/rotates (this also increases the frequency of the AC).	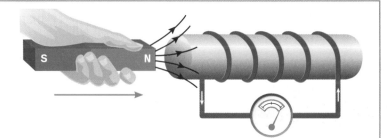
2 increasing the number of turns on the electromagnet's coils.	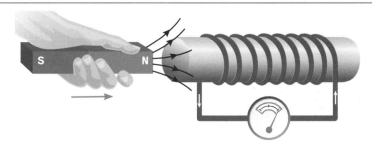
3 increasing the strength of the magnetic field.	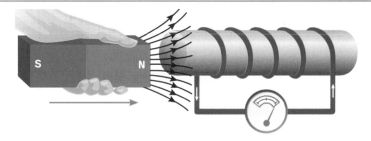

Quick Test

1. When a current-carrying wire is placed in a magnetic field it experiences a force and moves. What is this called?
2. What is meant by the dynamo effect?
3. At what frequency is mains electricity generated in the UK?

P6 Transforming

Transformers

A transformer is made of two coils of wire wound onto an iron core.

The two coils of wire aren't connected to each other. This enables the transformer to change the size of an alternating voltage.

A transformer only works with AC. It **doesn't** change AC to DC.

Step-up transformers:
- increase voltage
- have more turns on the secondary coil than on the primary coil.

Step-down transformers:
- decrease voltage
- have fewer turns on the secondary coil than on the primary coil
- are used in everyday applications, such as phone chargers, laptops and radios.

(HT) The voltage on the secondary coil can be calculated from the voltage on the primary coil (and vice versa) using the following equation:

Voltage across primary coil	=	No. primary turns
Voltage across secondary coil		No. secondary turns

Example
A laptop runs on 12V. If it's to be plugged into the mains (230V), a transformer is needed. If the transformer has 960 turns on the primary coil, how many turns does it have on the secondary coil?

$$\frac{V_p}{V_s} = \frac{N_p}{N_s}$$

$$N_s = \frac{N_p \times V_s}{V_p}$$

$$= \frac{960 \times 12}{230} = \textbf{50 turns}$$

(HT) Transformers and AC

Transformers can only use AC because they rely on a **changing** magnetic field in the primary coil to induce a voltage in the secondary coil. DC isn't suitable because it only provides a **steady** magnetic field.

As the AC **increases** in the primary coil, the magnetic field it produces grows and cuts through the wire of the secondary coil. This induces a current (to try to cancel out the magnetic field from the primary coil).

The current or voltage in a transformer can be calculated using the transformer equation opposite.

NB. This only applies if the transformer is 100% efficient.

$$V_p I_p = V_s I_s$$

Where: V_p = voltage in primary coil
I_p = current in primary coil
V_s = voltage in secondary coil
I_s = current in secondary coil

Example
If a current of 0.3 amps is supplied to a transformer in a laptop at a voltage of 230 volts, what current is fed to the laptop after the voltage has been stepped down to 12 volts?

$$V_p I_p = V_s I_s$$

$$230 \times 0.3 = 12 \times I_p$$

$$I_p = \frac{230 \times 0.3}{12} = \textbf{5.75A}$$

Transformers in the National Grid

When overhead power cables carry current, they get hot so energy is wasted as heat. This power loss can be reduced by reducing the current. The power loss in transmission relates to the current **squared**.

(HT) **Power loss = (Current²) × Resistance**

In a step-up transformer, if you increase the voltage, the current automatically decreases. Therefore, step-up transformers are used to increase the voltages from power stations to supply the National Grid.

Step-down transformers are used in sub-stations in order to reduce the voltages for domestic and commercial users.

(HT) The transformer equation shows that the power input to a transformer is equal to the power output of a transformer.

This means that in a step-up transformer, when the voltage is increased, the current is decreased in the same proportion. As a lower current will reduce power loss during transmission, using a step-up transformer at the power station reduces the energy lost as the current flows along the overhead cables.

A step-down transformer reduces the voltage to a safer level for consumers (but increases the current).

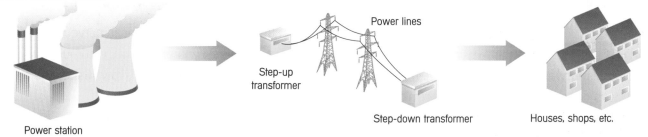

Power station

Step-up transformer

Power lines

Step-down transformer

Houses, shops, etc.

Isolating Transformers

An **isolating transformer** is used in some mains circuits, for example, bathroom shaver sockets, to make them safer.

In an isolating transformer, the two coils aren't connected to each other. This means that the user is isolated from the mains supply.

It's particularly important to use isolating transformers in areas such as bathrooms, so there's less chance of electrocution where there is water present.

(HT) An isolating transformer has equal numbers of turns on the primary and secondary coils. This makes no difference to the voltage.

The benefit of an isolating transformer is that it keeps the two halves of the circuit separate. Therefore, there is less risk of contact between the live parts (connected to the mains) and the earth lead (connected to the body of, for example, a shaver).

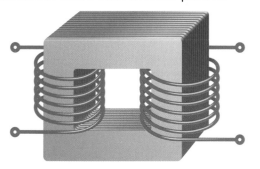

Quick Test

1. What type of transformer decreases voltage?
2. (HT) Write the transformer equation.

P6 Charging

Diodes

A silicon **diode** is a device that allows current to flow through it in one direction only.

A **current–voltage characteristic** can be drawn for a diode by plotting the current through the diode against the voltage across the diode.

From the example opposite, it can be seen that the current flows through the diode in one direction but not in the opposite direction.

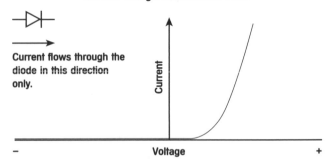

Current–Voltage Characteristic Curve

Current flows through the diode in this direction only.

Current

Voltage

–   +

(HT) A silicon diode is made of two types of silicon:
- **n-type**, which contains extra electrons (so has extra negative charge carriers)
- **p-type**, which has holes where there should be electrons (so the holes are like positive charge carriers).

A diode is **forward biased** in a circuit when the n-type is connected to the negative terminal of the battery. Current can flow because:
- the electrons can flow towards the holes
- the holes can flow towards the electrons.

If the diode is **reverse biased** ('backwards'), the current can't flow. This is because the electrons seem to drop into the holes and are unable to get past the layer between the two types of silicon.

The current–voltage characteristic curve shows that current flows easily in one direction through the diode. This is because it has a **low resistance** to current in this direction.

Current doesn't flow easily in the opposite direction because the diode has a **high resistance** to current flow in the reverse direction.

Half-Wave Rectification

If alternating current is passed through a single diode, the diode will allow the current flowing in one direction to pass through and will stop the current flowing in the opposite direction. This is half-wave rectification.

You should recognise half-wave rectification from a voltage–time graph.

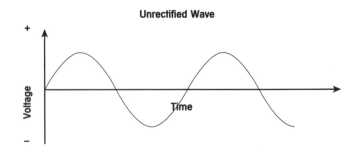

Unrectified Wave

+

Voltage

Time

–

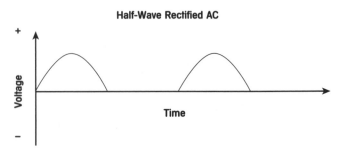

Half-Wave Rectified AC

+

Voltage

Time

–

Full-Wave Rectification

A group of four diodes can be connected together to make a **bridge circuit** to give full-wave rectification.

You should recognise full-wave rectification from a voltage–time graph.

HT A bridge circuit can supply full-wave rectification of AC. For each half of the AC cycle, there are two diodes that can pass the current, and send it to the output:
- Positive half cycle – current passes P, B, load, C then Q.
- Negative half cycle – current passes Q, D, load, A then P.

During each half cycle, the current passes through the load in the **same direction**.

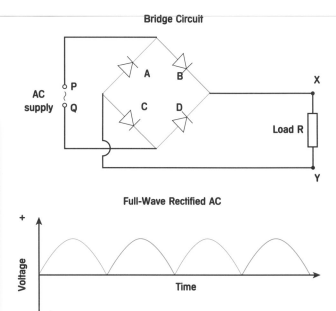

Bridge Circuit

Full-Wave Rectified AC

Capacitors

A capacitor stores charge that can be discharged later.

When current flows in a circuit containing an uncharged capacitor, the charge is stored on the capacitor and its pd increases.

When a charged capacitor is connected to a conductor, the capacitor behaves like a **battery**. The capacitor **discharges**, sending its stored current through the conductor.

HT When a charged capacitor is connected to a conductor, the flow of current from the capacitor to the conductor isn't steady. Instead the current flow decreases as the charge on the capacitor decreases.

As the charge on the capacitor decreases, the pd across the capacitor also decreases. This means that the pd across the conductor has decreased and so the current flowing decreases. This continues until the capacitor is fully discharged.

Simple Smoothing

A capacitor connected across a varying voltage supply produces a more **constant** (smoothed) output. This is useful for devices that need a more constant voltage supplied to them.

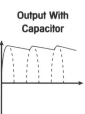

Input   Output Without   Output With
               Capacitor   Capacitor

HT A capacitor **smoothes** the output by discharging when the pd falls to a certain level, putting more charge into the circuit. This boosts the current so that it remains constant.

When the pd in the circuit is high enough, the capacitor charges up again. It remains charged until the pd falls and the capacitor has to make up the difference once more.

1 **a)** Three resistors with values 8Ω, 12Ω and 20Ω, are connected in series.
Calculate their total combined resistance. **[1]**

....

....

....

b) The resistors are now connected so that the 20Ω resistor was in one branch of a
parallel circuit and the 8Ω and 12Ω resistors were connected in series with each
other in the other branch of the circuit. Calculate the total resistance of this combination. **[3]**

....

....

....

2 Describe how you would increase the speed of an electric motor. **[3]**

....

....

....

....

3 **a)** What does the gradient of a voltage-current graph
represent? **[1]**

....

b) Describe the difference in resistance between the
two ohmic conductors. How do you know? **[2]**

....

....

4 **a)** How many diodes are required to produce full-wave rectification of an AC input? **[1]**

....

b) What is the name of the component used to 'smooth' a varying output voltage? **[1]**

....

5 A hairdryer powered by 230V has a resistance of 20Ω. How much current passes through
the hairdryer? **[2]**

....

6 **a)** Explain how transformers are used in the National Grid. **[4]**

....

....

....

b) How is an isolating transformer different from a step-up or step-down transformer? **[2]**

....

HT **7** Describe the benefits of miniaturisation of transistors and the limits affecting miniaturisation. **[4]**

....

....

....

8 A combination of logic gates is shown below. Construct the truth table for this combination of
logic gates. **[4]**

A	B	C	D	E	Q

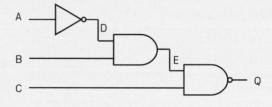

Answers

P1 Energy for the Home

Quick Test Answers

Page 6
1. Temperature °C, energy in joules
2. The yellow one.

Page 9
1. Double glazing
2. Light and sound.

Page 11
1. Number of complete waves passing a point each second.
2. **Any two from:** Ultraviolet; X-rays; Gamma rays
3. Gap size equals wavelength of wave.

Page 15
1. **Any two from:** Satellite communications; Mobile phones; Radar.
2. Water and fat.
3. It is totally internally reflected.

Page 18
1. S-Waves
2. True

Answers to Exam Practice Questions
1. a) The ice cream is melting.
   b) The energy needed to raise the temperature of 1kg of material by 1°C.

c) Energy transferred = Mass (kg) × specific heat capacity (J/kgC) × temperature change. 0.063kg × (1.67 × 10³) × 5 = 526J **[1 for calculation, 1 for correct answer]**
2. Efficiency = $\frac{20}{1000}$ = 0.2 or 20% **[1 for calculation, 1 for correct answer]**
3. Microwaves are absorbed **[1]** by the water/fat molecules **[1]** in the outside layers of the food. The heat energy is then transferred **[1]** throughout the rest of the food by conduction and convection **[1]**.
4. **A** Crest **B** Trough **C** Amplitude **D** Wavelength
5. 890 000 × 337 = 299 930 000 m/s or 300 000 000 m/s **[1 for calculation, 1 for correct answer]**
6. a) P-waves; S-waves b) S-waves
7. 6 mins × 20 = 120 mins = 2 hours **[1 for calculation, 1 for correct answer]**
8. a) 20 years; 30 years; 1.5 years
   b) **Any suitable suggestion with explanation,** e.g. Draft excluders because they have the lowest cost/shortest payback time; Double glazing because it has the biggest annual saving.
   c) Foil reflects **[1]** heat energy (infrared) **[1]** back into room/less heat loss **[1]** so he can turn radiators down **[1]**.

P2 Living for the Future (Energy Resources)

Quick Test Answers

Page 27
1. An energy resource that will not run out.
2. Surface area, light intensity and distance from the light source.
3. Burn fuel; Heat water to produce steam; Turn turbine; Turn generator.
4. **Any two from:** Carbon dioxide; Water vapour; Methane.

Page 30
1. Fossil fuels; Biomass; Nuclear.
2. The uranium fuel will run out.
3. Power = Current × Voltage

Page 32
1. Gamma
2. **Any two from:** To treat cancer; To sterilise medical equipment; In non-destructive testing; Tracers
3. Encased in glass, then placed in steel cylinders underground.

Page 37
1. Rock left over from the formation of the Universe.
2. A small body of frozen ice and dust.
3. A white dwarf.

Answers to Exam Practice Questions
1. a) He must wear protective clothing; He must use tongs and keep his distance from the radioactive materials; He needs to ensure only a short exposure time; All radioactive materials must be stored in shielded and labelled containers. **[Any three for 3]**
   b) Cosmic rays (from the sun and outer space); Radioactive substances in rocks, soil and living things
   c) i) Smoke alarms.
      ii) Tracer; Thickness gauge. **[Any one for 1]**

iii) Tracer; Treat cancer; Sterilise medical equipment. **[Any one for 1]**
2. a) Move it inside of a magnetic field.
   b) Use stronger magnets; Use more turns in the coil; Move the coil faster.
3. a) Efficiency = $\frac{50\,000}{150\,000}$ = 0.33 or 33% **[1 for calculation, 1 for correct answer]**
   b) Burn fuel, heat water to produce steam, steam turns turbine, turbine turns generator. **[All correct for 2]**
4. Craters; Sudden changes in fossil record; Unusual elements. **[Any two for 2]**
5. a) kWh = 1.2 × 0.25 = 0.3kWh **[1 for calculation, 1 for correct answer]**
   b) Power = $\frac{Energy}{Time}$ = $\frac{3kWh}{2\ hours}$ = 1.5kW or 1500W **[1 for calculation, 1 for correct answer]**
6. **This is a model answer, which demonstrates QWC and therefore would score the full 6 marks:** The Ptolemaic and Copernican models are similar in that they both proposed that the planets sat on glass spheres a fixed distance from the Sun, and that the stars were in fixed positions on the outermost sphere. The two models are different in that the Copernican model stated that the Sun was at the centre of the Universe, the Earth rotates once every 24 hours and the Earth takes one year to revolve around the Sun. In contrast, the Ptolemaic model stated that the Earth was the centre of the Universe.
7. Jupiter's huge gravity **[1]** pulls rocks apart so they don't combine **[1]**.

Answers

P3 Forces for Transport

Quick Test Answers
Page 41
1. Distance and time 2. Speed

Page 43
1. Acceleration = Change in speed ÷ Time taken
2. It is slowing down, deceleration at a rate of 5m/s^2

Page 49
1. ABS; Traction control; Cruise control; Paddle shifts.
2. A deflector.
3. It decreases.

Page 51
1. Weight and air resistance. 2. It stays the same.

Page 53
1. It quadruples. 2. 10N/kg 3. Joules (J)

Answers to Exam Practice Questions
1. a) Change in speed; Time taken
   b) Straight line with a positive gradient — Constant speed
      Straight line with a negative gradient — Deceleration
      Horizontal straight line — Acceleration
      [All correct for 2]

2. a) Graph line C
   b) At 45 mph, braking distance is 32m (**accept** 30–34m)
   c) Thinking distance is increased if the vehicle is travelling faster; If the driver is ill; If the driver is tired; If the driver is under the influence of alcohol or drugs.

3. a) Mass and Speed.
   b) Kinetic energy = 0.5 × 2000 × 20^2 = 400 000J **[1 for calculation, 1 for correct answer]**

4. Air bags; Crumple zones; Seatbelts; Safety cages. **[Any three for 3]**
5. A2; B4; C1; D3 **[All correct for 3]**
6. Height = $\frac{\text{Potential energy}}{(\text{mass} \times g)}$ = $\frac{30}{(0.16 \times 10)}$ = 18.75m **[1 for calculation, 1 for correct answer]**

7. a) Change in momentum = $m_1v_1 - m_2v_2$ = (1100 × 22.3)− (1100 × 13.4) = 24530 − 14740 = 9790kgm/s **[1 for calculation, 1 for correct answer]**
   b) i) Change in momentum = $m_1v_1 - m_2v_2$ = (1100 × 13.4)− (1100 × 0) = 14740kgm/s **[1 for calculation, 1 for correct answer]**
      ii) Force = change in momentum ÷ time = 14740 ÷ 2.2 = 6700N **[1 for calculation, 1 for correct answer]**

8. h = v^2 ÷ 2g; v^2 = 2gh = 2 × 10 × 30 = 600
   v = $\sqrt{600}$ = 24.5m/s. **[2 for calculation, 1 for correct answer]**

P4 Radiation for Life

Quick Test Answers
Page 58
1. Positive and negative.
2. Re-start a heart which has stopped.
3. Lose electrons.

Page 61
1. R = $\frac{V}{I}$
2. Live – brown; Neutral – blue; Earth – green and yellow.
3. Melts and breaks.
4. Fires (flex overheating); Injury to user; Damage to components.

Page 63
1. The number of waves that pass a point in 1 second.
2. **Any two from:** Scanning the body; Breaking down kidney stones; Measuring the speed of blood flow; Foetal scanning.
3. It can be used to look at soft tissue and it does not damage living cells.

Page 66
1. By the number of nuclear decays emitted per second.
2. False
3. A helium nucleus (made up of two protons and two neutrons).
4. A proton and an electron.

Page 71
1. Alpha, beta and gamma.
2. Gamma
3. Beta

Answers to Exam Practice Questions
1. a) False. Electrons have a negative charge.
   b) Spray-painting; Smoke precipitators; Defibrillators **[Any two for 2]**

2. a) Neutral — Green and yellow
      Earth — Brown
      Live — Blue   **[All correct for 2]**
   b) False. They still require a fuse to protect the appliance.

3. a) R = $\frac{V}{I}$ = $\frac{12}{0.3}$ = 40 ohms **[1 for calculation, 1 for correct answer]**
   b) I = $\frac{V}{R}$ = $\frac{12}{80}$ = 0.15A **[1 for calculation, 1 for correct answer]**

4. **This is a model answer, which demonstrates QWC and therefore would score the full 6 marks:** Nuclear fusion is the process by which heat energy is released when nuclei fuse together, for example in stars and fusion bombs. A large amount of heat energy is released. Nuclear fusion can only happen at extremely high temperatures. However, it is very difficult to manage such high temperatures, which means that nuclear fusion is not yet a possible energy resource on Earth.

5. a) 8 days
   b) Yes, caesium-137 has a half-life of 30 years; so after only four months it is still extremely radioactive; and poses a severe health hazard.

P5 Space for Reflection

Quick Test Answers
Page 75
1. Natural – moon; Artificial – **Any one from:** Communication; Weather; Military satellite.
2. It increases. 3. 24 hours

Page 81
1. Scalar – **any two from:** Mass; Energy; Speed; Time. Vector – **any two from:** Velocity; Force; Acceleration.
2. Momentum = Mass × Velocity
3. It reduces the force required to act and reduces the injuries caused.

Page 83
1. 1m–10km
2. It reduces their strength or stops them.
3. They travel more slowly through the ionised gas in the ionosphere.
4. Radio waves have very long wavelength.

Page 89
1. The distance between the centre of the lens and the focal point.
2. Blue / violet light

Answers

Answers to Exam Practice Questions

1. **a)** B **Should be ticked**.
   b) They orbit high above he Earth; They take 24 hours to complete one orbit; In fixed position above Earth's surface **[Any two for 2]**
2. **a)** Average speed $= \frac{\text{Total distance}}{\text{Total time taken}} = \frac{6000}{600} = 10\text{m/s}$ **[1 for calculation, 1 for correct answer]**
   b) $70 - 60 = 10\text{km/h}$
   c) Scalar, because it has size only.
3. **a)** **Horizontal** – Constant velocity; **Vertical** – Projectile accelerates.
   b) Speed $= \frac{\text{distance}}{\text{time}}$
   Time $= \frac{\text{distance}}{\text{speed}}$
   Time $= \frac{18}{6}$
   Time $= 3\text{s}$ **[1 for calculation, 1 for correct answer]**
   c) $s = ut + \frac{1}{2}at^2$
   $s = (0 \times 3) + (\frac{1}{2} \times 10 \times 3^2)$
   $s = 0 + 45$
   $s = 45\text{m}$ **[2 for calculation, 1 for correct answer]**

4. Momentum = Mass × Velocity = $(200 + 50) \times 30 = 7500\text{kg m/s}$ **[1 for calculation, 1 for correct answer]**
5. **a)** **i)** It is being refracted.
      ii) The waves travel from one medium to another; This causes the wave speed to decrease; and the wave to change direction.
   b) Refractive index $= \frac{\text{speed of light in vacuum}}{\text{speed of light in medium}}$
      Refractive index $= \frac{3 \times 10^8}{2 \times 10^8} = \frac{3}{2}$
      Refractive index = 1.5 **[1 for calculation, 1 for correct answer]**
6. **This is a model answer, which demonstrates QWC and therefore would score the full 6 marks:** Waves can interfere constructively, which is known as constructive interference or reinforcement. This happens when identical waves arrive at a point in phase. The result is a wave with a larger amplitude and bright fringes can be seen.
   Waves can also interfere destructively, which is known as destructive interference or cancellation. This happens when identical waves arrive at a point out of phase. The result is a wave with an amplitude of zero, and dark fringes can be seen.

Quick Test Answers
Page 95
1. Resistance increases.
2. Series
3. It decreases.
Page 99
1. Both inputs 'high' or 1.
2. It uses a small current to switch on a large current.
3. NOR gate
Page 103
1. The motor effect.
2. Generating electricity.
3. 50Hz
Page 105
1. Step-down transformer
2. $V_p I_p = V_s I_s$

Answers to Exam Practice Questions
1. **a)** $R_T = 8 + 12 + 20$
   $R_T = 40\Omega$
   b) Resistance of 8Ω and 12Ω resistors combined $= 20\Omega$
   $\frac{1}{R_T} = \frac{1}{20} + \frac{1}{20}$
   $\frac{1}{R_T} = \frac{2}{20}$
   $R_T = \frac{20}{2}$
   $R_T = 10\Omega$ **[2 for calculation, 1 for correct answer]**
2. Increase number of coils; Increase magnetic field; Increase electric current.
3. **a)** Resistance.
   b) Ohmic conductor B has a greater resistance; Because it has a greater gradient.
4. **a)** Four
   b) Capacitor
5. Current $= \frac{\text{Voltage}}{\text{Resistance}} = \frac{230}{20} = 11.5\text{A}$ **[1 for calculation, 1 for correct answer]**

6. **a)** Step-up transformers are used from power stations to supply the National Grid; to increase voltage so that current is reduced in overhead power lines; However, the voltage is too high for domestic and commercial users so step-down transformers are used in sub-stations; to reduce the voltage before it reaches homes and offices.
   b) An isolating transformer has an equal number of turns **[1]** on the primary and secondary coils **[1]**. (Voltage out equals voltage in)
7. Benefits: Increases the number of transistors that can be connected in a processor; Means computer processors can be made smaller. **[2]**
   Limitations: Smaller components give out more heat as a current passes through; The thinner they are, the less resistance they offer (quantum tunnelling). **[2]**
8.

A	B	C	D	E	Q
0	0	0	1	0	1
0	0	1	1	0	1
0	1	0	1	1	1
0	1	1	1	1	0
1	0	0	0	0	1
1	0	1	0	0	1
1	1	0	0	0	1
1	1	1	0	0	1

[$\frac{1}{2}$ mark for every correct row]

Acceleration – the rate at which an object changes its velocity.

Air resistance – the frictional force that acts on a moving object.

Alternating current (AC) – an electric current that changes direction of flow repeatedly.

Amplitude – the maximum disturbance of a wave from a central position.

Analogue – signal that varies continuously in amplitude/frequency.

Attraction – the drawing together of materials with different charges.

Big Bang Theory – theory of how the Universe started.

Binary – digital signals.

Black hole – formed at the end of a star's life, has a very dense core which light cannot escape from.

Braking distance – the distance a car travels during braking to a stop.

Capacitor – an electrical device that accumulates and temporarily stores electrical charge; used for smoothing AC.

Centripetal force – the external force towards the centre of a circle required to make an object follow a circular path at a constant speed.

Circuit breaker – electrical switch which protects a circuit from damage.

Compression – area of high pressure in a medium caused by a wave, e.g. sound.

Conduction – transfer of thermal or electrical energy.

Conductor – material that transfers thermal or electrical energy.

Convection – transfer of heat energy without the movement of the substance.

Convex lens – a lens that causes light rays passing through it to meet at a point (converge).

Critical angle – the largest incident angle at which refraction can occur.

Current – the rate of flow of an electrical charge; measured in amperes (A).

Data – information collected from an experiment/investigation.

Deforestation – destruction of forests by cutting down trees.

Degrees Celsius (°C) – unit of temperature.

Diffraction – the spreading out of a wave as a result of passing an obstacle through a gap.

Digital – signal that uses only 1s and 0s.

Diode – an electrical device that allows electric current to flow in one direction only.

Direct current (DC) – an electric current that only flows in one direction.

Dispersion – (of light) the separation of light into different wavelengths, which represent the colours of the rainbow (visible spectrum).

Distance–Time graph – a graph showing distance travelled against time taken; the gradient of the line represents speed.

Dynamo effect – generating electricity by moving a coil of wire near a magnet.

Earthed – connecting the metal case of an electrical appliance to the earth wire of a plug.

Efficiency – useful output energy expressed as a percentage of total input energy.

Electromagnetic – energy transmitted as waves.

Electromagnetic waves – includes radio waves, visible light and gamma, all of which can travel through a vacuum at the speed of light.

Electron – a negatively charged particle that orbits the nucleus of an atom.

Energy – ability to do work; measured in joules.

Focal length – a measure of how strongly an optical system focuses or diverges.

Focal point – the point at which all light rays parallel to the axis of the lens converge.

Force – a push or pull acting on an object; measured in newtons (N).

Fossil fuel – coal, oil and natural gas.

Frequency – the number of waves produced (or that pass a particular point) in one second.

Friction – the resistive force between two surfaces as they move over each other.

Full-wave rectification – the whole of an input current is converted to a constant polarity (positive or negative) at its output.

Fuse – a thin piece of metal, which overheats and melts to break an electric circuit if it's overloaded.

Global warming – increase in average temperature on Earth due to rise in CO_2 in the atmosphere.

Gravitational force – a force of attraction between masses.

Gravitational potential energy (GPE) – the energy an object has because of its mass and height above the Earth.

Glossary of Key Words

Gravity (gravitational force) – a force of attraction between masses.

Half-life – the time taken for half the atoms in radioactive material to decay.

Half-wave rectification – either the positive or negative half of an AC wave is allowed to pass through a diode, while the other half is blocked.

Hypothesis – a scientific explanation that will be tested through experiments.

Insulator – a substance that doesn't transfer thermal or electrical energy.

Interference – when a signal is corrupted, e.g. hissing on the radio.

Ion – a charged particle formed when an atom gains or loses an electron.

Ionising – radiation that turns atoms into ions.

Ionosphere – a layer of charged particles in the Earth's atmosphere.

Joule (J) – unit of energy.

Kilowatt hour – a measure of how much electrical energy has been used.

Kinetic energy (KE) – the energy possessed by a body because of its movement.

Laser – perfectly coherent light source.

Logic gate – a device in a circuit that performs operations on input signals.

Longitudinal wave – a wave where the particles vibrate in the direction of energy transfer.

Magnetic field – the area of effect of a magnet (or the Earth) indicated by lines of force surrounding the magnet (or the Earth).

Magnification – enlarging the size of an image; measured as $\frac{\text{image size}}{\text{object size}}$.

Mass – the quantity of matter in an object.

Model – a representation of a system or idea, used to describe or explain the system or idea.

Momentum – a measure of the state of motion of an object as a product of its mass and velocity.

Nuclear – non-renewable fuel.

Nuclear fission – the splitting of atomic nuclei.

Nuclear fusion – the release of heat energy when two nuclei join together.

Orbit – the path of an object around a larger object.

Orbital period – the time it takes an object to make one complete orbit.

Parabolic – curved path taken by a projectile.

Payback time – the time taken for insulation to pay for itself from savings made.

Photocell – a device that captures light energy and transforms it into electrical energy.

Polarisation – the blocking of light waves that oscillate in certain directions, for example, to cut out glare.

Pollution – the contamination of an environment by chemicals, waste or heat.

Potential difference (voltage) – the difference in potential between two points in an electrical circuit; the energy transferred in a circuit by each Coulomb of charge; measured in volts (V).

Power – the rate of doing work; measured in watts (W).

Projectile – an object that's projected forward, for example, fired into the air.

Radiation – electromagnetic waves/particles emitted by a radioactive substance.

Radioactive – substance that emits radiation from its atomic nuclei.

Radioisotope – a radioactive isotope of an element.

Rarefaction – area of low pressure in a medium caused by a wave, e.g. sound.

Real image – an image produced by rays of light meeting at a point; can be projected onto a screen.

Red giant – a stage in the life cycle of stars – they expand to form a red giant.

Reflection – change in direction of a wave at a boundary between two media.

Refraction – change in direction of a light ray as it passes from one medium to another and changes speed.

Refractive index – a measure of a medium's ability to bend light due to slowing the light down.

Relative speed – the speed of an object, relative to another object that is being treated to be at rest.

Relay – an electrical device that uses a small current in one circuit to make or break a connection in another circuit where a larger current flows.

Renewable – energy sources that will not run out.

Repulsion – the pushing away of materials that have the same charge.

Resistance – how hard it is to get a current through a component at a particular potential difference; measured in ohms (Ω).

Satellite – an object that orbits a planet.

Scalar quantity – a quantity where there is only size.

Seismic wave – wave produced by an earthquake.

Specific heat capacity – value of how much energy a material can hold. Heat required to change temperature of 1 kg by 1°C.

Specific latent heat – heat energy required to melt or boil 1kg of a material.

Speed – the rate at which an object moves.

Speed–Time graph – a graph showing speed against time; the gradient of the line represents acceleration.

Static electricity – build up of charge in a substance.

Terminal speed – a steady falling speed, when the weight of an object is equal and opposite to the air resistance on it.

Thermogram – using colours to represent temperatures.

Thinking distance – the distance that a car travels whilst the driver reacts and starts to brake.

Total internal reflection – complete reflection of a light or infrared ray back into a medium.

Tracer – a radioactive substance that can be followed and detected.

Trajectory – the path of a moving body.

Transfer – moving energy from one place to another.

Transform – changing energy from one form to another, e.g. kinetic to electrical.

Transformer – an electrical device that changes the voltage of alternating currents.

Transverse wave – a wave in which the vibrations are at 90° to the direction of wave travel.

Ultrasound – sound waves with a frequency above 20 000Hz.

Variable – something that changes during the course of an experiment/investigation.

Vector quantity – a quantity where both size and direction are known.

Velocity – an object's rate of displacement or speed in a particular direction.

Voltage (potential difference) – the difference in potential between two points in an electrical circuit; the energy transferred in a circuit by each Coulomb of charge; measured in volts (V).

Wavelength – the distance between corresponding points on two adjacent disturbances.

Weight – the gravitational force that pulls an object towards the centre of the Earth.

White dwarf – a stage in the life cycle of some stars; medium-sized stars will collapse to form a white dwarf.

Fleming's Left Hand Rule – rule used to work out the direction of force on a wire.

Free electron – loosely bound electron in outer shell of atom which is able to move through metals.

Isotope – one or more atoms with the same atomic number but different mass numbers.

Light year – the distance light travels in one year.

Multiplexing – method of sending more than one signal at a time.

Red shift – lengthening of a wave as a result of an object moving further away in space.

Thermonuclear fusion – the joining together of small atomic nuclei to make a larger nucleus; releasing energy.

Virtual image – an image produced by rays of light appearing to come from a point; can't be projected onto a screen.

Notes

Key

| relative atomic mass |
| **atomic symbol** |
| name |
| atomic (proton) number |

| 1 | H | hydrogen | 1 |

1	2											3	4	5	6	7	0
																	4 **He** helium 2
7 **Li** lithium 3	9 **Be** beryllium 4											11 **B** boron 5	12 **C** carbon 6	14 **N** nitrogen 7	16 **O** oxygen 8	19 **F** fluorine 9	20 **Ne** neon 10
23 **Na** sodium 11	24 **Mg** magnesium 12											27 **Al** aluminium 13	28 **Si** silicon 14	31 **P** phosphorus 15	32 **S** sulfur 16	35.5 **Cl** chlorine 17	40 **Ar** argon 18
39 **K** potassium 19	40 **Ca** calcium 20	45 **Sc** scandium 21	48 **Ti** titanium 22	51 **V** vanadium 23	52 **Cr** chromium 24	55 **Mn** manganese 25	56 **Fe** iron 26	59 **Co** cobalt 27	59 **Ni** nickel 28	63.5 **Cu** copper 29	65 **Zn** zinc 30	70 **Ga** gallium 31	73 **Ge** germanium 32	75 **As** arsenic 33	79 **Se** selenium 34	80 **Br** bromine 35	84 **Kr** krypton 36
85 **Rb** rubidium 37	88 **Sr** strontium 38	89 **Y** yttrium 39	91 **Zr** zirconium 40	93 **Nb** niobium 41	96 **Mo** molybdenum 42	[98] **Tc** technetium 43	101 **Ru** ruthenium 44	103 **Rh** rhodium 45	106 **Pd** palladium 46	108 **Ag** silver 47	112 **Cd** cadmium 48	115 **In** indium 49	119 **Sn** tin 50	122 **Sb** antimony 51	128 **Te** tellurium 52	127 **I** iodine 53	131 **Xe** xenon 54
133 **Cs** caesium 55	137 **Ba** barium 56	139 **La*** lanthanum 57	178 **Hf** hafnium 72	181 **Ta** tantalum 73	184 **W** tungsten 74	186 **Re** rhenium 75	190 **Os** osmium 76	192 **Ir** iridium 77	195 **Pt** platinum 78	197 **Au** gold 79	201 **Hg** mercury 80	204 **Tl** thallium 81	207 **Pb** lead 82	209 **Bi** bismuth 83	[209] **Po** polonium 84	[210] **At** astatine 85	[222] **Rn** radon 86
[223] **Fr** francium 87	[226] **Ra** radium 88	[227] **Ac*** actinium 89	[261] **Rf** rutherfordium 104	[262] **Db** dubnium 105	[266] **Sg** seaborgium 106	[264] **Bh** bohrium 107	[277] **Hs** hassium 108	[268] **Mt** meitnerium 109	[271] **Ds** darmstadtium 110	[272] **Rg** roentgenium 111							

Elements with atomic numbers 112–116 have been reported but not fully authenticated

*The lanthanoids (atomic numbers 58–71) and the actinoids (atomic numbers 90–103) have been omitted.

Index